of the worlds

Illustrated by **Paolo D'Altan**

Member of CISQ Federation

CERTIFIED MANAGEMENT SYSTEM
ISO 9001

The design, production and distribution of educational materials
for the CIDEB (Black Cat) brand are managed in compliance
with the rules of Quality Management System which fulfils
the requirements of the standard ISO 9001

Content editor: Chiara Blau
Editor: Marcella De Meglio (Studio Zebra)
Design: Daniele Pagliari, Silvia Bassi
Page Layout: Annalisa Possenti
Picture research: Alice Graziotin

Art Director: Carla Nadia Maestri

Picture credits:
Shutterstock; iStockPhoto; Adobe Stock; Time Life Pictures/
Mansell/The LIFE Picture Collection via Getty Images: 4;
Mondadori via Getty Images: 39; NY Daily News Archive via Getty
Images: 82, 83; CBS Photo Archive/Getty Images: 84-85;
Mondadori Portfolio/©Paramount/Courtesy Everett Collection: 106.

We would be happy to give you further information
concerning our material and receive your comments.

info@blackcat-cideb.com
blackcat-cideb.com

Printed in Genoa, Italy, by Litoprint srl

Contents

PRELIMINARY   This icon indicates Preliminary-style activities

T: GRADE **6** This icon indicates Trinity-style activities

 n. track   THE STORY IS FULLY RECORDED.

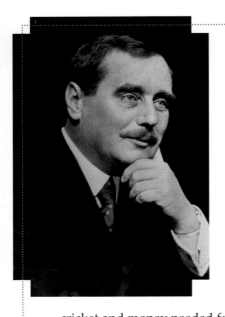

H.G. Wells

Herbert George Wells was born in Bromley, in the south of England. He was often unwell as a child and his parents worried that he might die at a young age, like his older sister. The family had a shop and his father made extra money by playing professional cricket. When Wells was thirteen, his father fell off a ladder and broke his leg. With no income[1] from cricket and money needed for doctor's bills, the family was bankrupt.[2] Wells' mother became a housekeeper at a country house and Wells became an apprentice.[3] He hated it and at the age of sixteen he got a job as a teacher's assistant. Wells became a passionate reader and when he visited his mother he was able to read books in the library of the country house. He loved the work of Jonathan Swift and Voltaire. Eventually Wells won a scholarship to what is now the Royal College of Science, in Kensington, London. He studied with Thomas Huxley, a supporter of Darwin, and spent most of his free time editing the student magazine.

Wells got a job as a science teacher in a small private school and later found regular work as a journalist and theatre critic. He published his novel *The Time Machine* (1895) in instalments[4] in a small evening newspaper. This novel brought him success and fame.

---

1. **income** : money received annually for a job.
2. **bankrupt** : unable to pay debts.
3. **apprentice** : a person who learns a trade.
4. **instalments** : a novel published in several parts.

Wells is known as one of the founding fathers of science fiction, but he preferred to call his work 'scientific romances'. Examples of his work in this genre are *The Island of Doctor Moreau* (1896), *The Invisible Man* (1897), *The War of the Worlds* (1898) and *In the Days of the Comet* (1906). He also wrote humorous novels, which were partly autobiographical, describing the social conditions at the end of the 19th century: *Love and Mr Lewisham* (1900), *Tono-Bungay* (1909) and *The History of Mr Polly* (1910).

Behind his imagination and inventiveness lay his passionate concerns for man and society. Wells supported socialist ideals and explored issues of class in his novel *Kipps* (1905), which was one of his favourite works.

Wells was a member of the Fabian Society, a British socialist organisation, and became active in politics. He visited Russia in 1920 and 1934 and met Lenin and Stalin.

Wells wrote until the very end of his life, but his feelings became darker. In his novel *The World Set Free* (1913) he described a Utopia after the invention of a bomb which caused mass destruction and in his essay *Mind at the End of It's Tether* (1945) he considered the end of humanity.

Comprehension check

1 **Answer the questions.**

1 In what way did Wells' family have financial problems?
2 What subject did Wells teach? Why could this have been useful in his writing?
3 How was his novel *The Time Machine* published?
4 What did Wells like to call his science-fiction work?
5 Who did Wells meet in 1920 and 1934?
6 How did Wells feelings become darker towards the end of his life?

The characters

The narrator's brother

The narrator's wife

The narrator

The curate

The Martians

Before you read

Vocabulary

1 **Match the words (1-15) to the correct meaning (a-o).**

1	Martian	a	person who studies planets and stars
2	Mars	b	a three dimensional shape
3	meteor	c	the area outside the atmosphere of the Earth
4	space	d	the second smallest planet in the solar system
5	meteorite	e	a heavy weapon used in battles
6	astronomer	f	a force that pulls and keeps you on the ground
7	cannon	g	a high temperature
8	canister	h	a creature which lives on Planet Mars
9	telescope	i	a metal box
10	cylinder	j	a cover for a container
11	volcanic explosion	k	a rock from space that lands on Earth
12	heat	l	when hot lava comes out of a volcano
13	flash	m	a short sudden burst of light
14	lid	n	looks like a shooting star
15	gravity	o	an instrument to look at the stars

2 **Match the words to the parts of the picture.**

> tentacles oily skin disc-like eyes V-shaped mouth

1 ....

2 ....

3 ....

4 ....

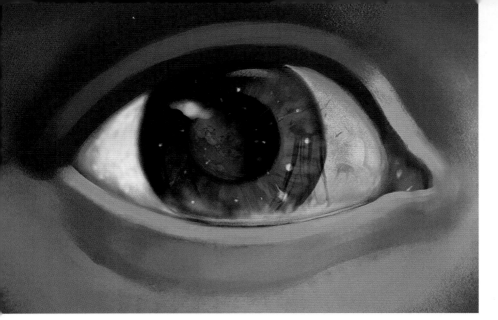

The falling star

I am a philosopher and a writer and in the last few years I have realised that intelligences, greater than man, are watching our world. Planet Mars is older than Earth and anyone living there is certainly more advanced.

There is air and water to support life on planet Mars, but it receives only half of the light and heat from the sun that Earth gets. However, most humans don't think space is a danger. Men often wonder if there is life on Mars, but they are certain that people living there are inferior to humans. No one thought that superior beings wanted to leave their planet and take control of Earth. No one knew that these superior creatures were already making plans.

The climate on Mars was becoming too cold and the air was thin. This was why the Martians turned their attention to Earth.

They looked across space with their instruments. They saw a warmer planet, green with vegetation and with narrow seas. They liked this rich planet called Earth.

For several years, astronomers have noticed strange lights on the surface of Mars and have described it as jets[1] of fire, like a gas flame. They didn't know that the jets of fire came from huge canons on Mars, which were firing canisters with Martians inside to Earth.

My friend Ogilvy, an astronomer, showed me the planet Mars through his telescope. I saw a red flash of fire from the distant planet. Ogilvy thought meteors were falling or the flashes came from a huge volcanic explosion. The newspapers wrote about these explosions, but no one seemed to be worried about this development and everyone went about their daily lives. My friend Ogilvy didn't believe there was anything man-like on Mars. One bright, clear night I pointed out the planets and stars to my wife. The sky seemed beautiful and safe. We had no idea what was coming.

One night there was a falling star. It fell in the country, quite near where I lived. My friend Ogilvy said it was a meteor and went out looking for it. He was shocked when he found a huge cylinder lying in an enormous sandy hole. It was almost completely buried[2] in sand and he was surprised by the size of the cylinder. It was about thirty metres across and it was still hot from the flight. Ogilvy wanted to have a closer look, but when he climbed into the hole, he heard sounds and saw the

---

1.   **jet** : a thin stream of something like water or fire.
2.   **bury** : put under the ground.

circular top of the cylinder moving. Someone inside was trying to break out.

'Good heavens,' said Ogilvy. 'There are men inside who need to get out. They could be burned from the heat inside the cylinder and trying to escape.' And suddenly he linked this huge thing that had fallen to earth with the flashes he had seen on Mars.

Ogilvy moved forward, but the heat was too strong. He had to get help. Ogilvy ran into town, but when he told people his strange story, no one believed him. Ogilvy had lost his hat and his appearance was so wild that most people thought he was a madman. Only Henderson, a London journalist, believed him.

'Henderson,' Ogilvy said. 'You saw the shooting star last night, didn't you?'

'I did.'

'Well, it's on Horsell Common now.'

'So, a meteorite landed there?' said Henderson.

'It's more than a meteorite. It's a huge cylinder and there's something inside.' Ogilvy told Henderson what he had seen. The two men ran to Horsell Common and found the cylinder lying in the same position. Now they could see a thin circle of bright metal between the top and the body of the cylinder. As air entered or escaped there was a thin sound. The two men hit the burned cylinder with a stick, but there was no answer. The man or men inside were probably dead.

Ogilvy and Henderson went back to the town to get help. They ran up the street in the bright sunlight as shops and bedroom windows were opening. Henderson sent a message to London with the news and by eight o'clock a group of people went to Horsell Common to see the 'dead men from Mars.'

I went there too and found a group of about twenty people looking down at the cylinder in the huge hole. Some went away and more people came. I climbed into the hole and thought I heard some sounds of movement. The cylinder looked old, but as I came closer I saw that the yellowish-white metal was not like any metal found on Earth. My mind was clear. This flying object had come from planet Mars.

The early editions of the evening papers had surprised London with the headlines:

A MESSAGE RECEIVED FROM MARS
STRANGE STORY
FROM THE TOWN OF WOKING

By evening the crowd had become quite large. Men were digging[3] in the hole and we could see most of the cylinder. The sun was setting and the large crowd looked black against the lemon-yellow of the sky. Stent, the Astronomer Royal, was there, asking the crowd to keep back.

A boy ran towards me. 'It's moving,' he said to me. 'It's turning and opening and I don't like it. I'm going home.'

There was a strange humming [4] sound coming from the

---

3.   **to dig :**

4.   **to hum :** to sing with closed lips a sound like a bee.

cylinder in the hole and the crowd seemed very excited. The sun was in my eyes as the lid of the cylinder fell onto the ground. I think everyone expected to see a man, but a creature appeared with two great disc-like eyes. It had tentacles like little grey snakes. I felt suddenly cold and a woman screamed behind me. The expression on the faces of the crowd[5] changed to horror and I couldn't move.

A grey creature about the size of a bear got slowly out of the cylinder. Its skin was brown and oily and it had a strange V-shaped mouth and no chin. It stared at me with its dark eyes and its movements were slow and painful because of the difference in gravity. I looked at it and I felt fear and disgust.

People watching looked surprised, then horrified as another creature climbed out from inside the cylinder. With a thick cry it jumped into the hole and I ran away fast towards the trees. A man who had fallen into the hole was unable to escape. We heard a faint scream, then silence.

---

5.   **crowd** : a large group of people.

The text and *beyond*

Comprehension check

1 **PRELIMINARY** **For each question choose the correct answer (a, b, c or d).**

1 The narrator is
   a ☐ a scientist.
   b ☐ an astronomer.
   c ☐ an author and a thinker.
   d ☐ an astrologist.

2 Planet Mars is
   a ☐ hotter and brighter than Earth.
   b ☐ colder and darker than Earth.
   c ☐ the same temperature as Earth.
   d ☐ cold and completely dark.

3 For a long time astronomers watching Mars have noticed
   a ☐ parts of the planet burning.
   b ☐ red flashes of fire.
   c ☐ no light.
   d ☐ blue flashes of fire.

4 One day something falls to Earth, it's
   a ☐ a falling star.
   b ☐ a meteor.
   c ☐ a piece of rock.
   d ☐ a huge cylinder.

5 When Ogilvy first tells people his story they
   a ☐ think he's crazy.
   b ☐ are scared.
   c ☐ believe him.
   d ☐ run to help.

2 Ogilvy and Henderson run for help. Are the sentences true (T) or false (F)?

	T	F
1 Henderson and Ogilvy are sure that the men from Mars are dead.	☐	☐
2 The cylinder is made from a metal found on Earth.	☐	☐
3 An astronomer asks the crowds to come closer to the cylinder.	☐	☐
4 The cylinder begins to move and open.	☐	☐
5 No sound is coming from the cylinder.	☐	☐
6 The crowd is expectant but suddenly they become afraid.	☐	☐

3 Complete the sentences with the characters from the box. You can use some character more than once.

Henderson Ogilvy the narrator a boy a Martian

1 .... thought other intelligences were watching Planet Earth.

2 .... watched Mars through his telescope.

3 .... didn't believe that anything living on Mars was like Man.

4 .... thought a meteorite had landed on Horsell Common.

5 .... climbed into the hole and heard sounds of movement.

6 .... was afraid of the cylinder and decided to go home.

7 .... stared at the narrator with its dark eyes.

8 .... felt fear and disgust when he saw the Martians.

Predicting the story

4 In pairs, discuss the questions.

1 Do you think the Martians are friendly or hostile? Why?

2 What do you think will happen next?

Grammar

Comparatives

*Planet Mars is **older** than Earth and anyone living there is certainly **more advanced.***

We use comparative adjectives to describe people and things.

We use *than* with a comparative when we compare two things.

Short adjectives with one syllable add -*er*:

*cold — col**der***

Adjectives that end with a vowel and a consonant double the consonant and add -*er*:

*big — big**ger***

Adjectives that end in -*y* change -*y* to -*i* and add -*er*:

*heavy — heav**ier***

Adjectives with two, three or four syllables add *more*:

*excited — **more** excited*

Some adjectives are irregular:

*good — **better***

*bad — **worse***

*far — **farther***

---

5 **Complete the sentences with the correct comparative adjective.**

1 The Martians were .... (+, *advanced*) than the people on Earth.

2 The air is .... (+, *thin*) on Mars than on Earth.

3 Earth is .... (+, *green*) than Mars.

4 The cylinder was .... (+, *hot*) than Ogilvy expected and the heat .... (+, *strong*).

5 The cylinder was .... (+, *big*) than a meteorite.

6 The creatures' movements were .... (+, *slow*) and .... (+, *painful*) than the movements of people on Earth.

Before you read

Vocabulary

1 **Match the words (a-f) to the pictures (1-6).**

a hand in hand   **d** deadly white

b side by side   **e** flag

c set on fire   **f** searchlight

2 **Match the words (1-8) to the correct meaning (a-h).**

1	still	**a**	part of a tree
2	dusk	**b**	not able to stay still
3	strength	**c**	physical energy
4	branch	**d**	evening — before it becomes dark
5	restless	**e**	calm
6	hissing	**f**	electricity in the sky
7	hammering	**g**	the sound of a metal tool hitting something
8	lightning	**h**	making a long s sound

The cylinder opens

felt a strange kind of interest in the Martians and I wanted to see them again. I was afraid and curious, but in the end my curiosity won. I wanted to look into the hole, so I walked in a big curve until I could see tentacles, like the arms of an octopus, waving near the cylinder. I saw a Martian lift a thin stick with something that looked like a mirror on one end, which turned and moved. What were the creatures doing? Most of the people were standing in groups and I noticed a neighbour of mine.

track 03

'What ugly creatures,' he said over and over again. 'What strange men from Mars.' We stood watching side by side and then I climbed a small sand hill to get a better view. As the sun disappeared people started walking slowly towards the hole. They moved, stopped, watched and moved again. I went a little closer.

A larger group of people, including Ogilvy, Stent and Henderson were moving towards the cylinder carrying a white flag. They had decided these creatures were intelligent, despite their horrible appearance. They wanted to show the Martians that humans were intelligent too.

Suddenly there were three flashes of light and some green smoke. I could hear a hissing sound, which changed to a humming noise and a black shape rose up [1] out of the cylinder. There were some strange flashes of heat and many people in the group carrying the flag were turned to flame. I saw them fall. Each man lay dead on the dark, smoking earth. The others ran away. Then the hissing and humming stopped and the black shape disappeared.

It had all happened so quickly as I stood silent and still. The flashes of light had killed so many people, but I was still alive. I couldn't see any Martians and the only visible thing was the stick with a mirror on the end.

Suddenly I felt real fear. I turned and ran. I was afraid of the Martians, but also of the dusk and the stillness around me. I ran crying silently like a child and I did not look back, afraid that this mysterious death, fast as light, could jump out and kill me.

I thought about the heat-ray as I hurried home. It could kill quickly and silently by using intense heat to destroy. About forty people lay dead near the hole, but many had escaped. Later, people from neighbouring towns, who hadn't heard about the deaths, came to see the cylinder. The Martians attacked them too, but they were lucky. A low sandy hill saved them when the Martians

---

1. **rise up** : move to a higher position.

turned the heat-ray on the crowd. The heat-ray went above their heads setting the tops of the trees on fire. Burning branches fell onto the road and people screamed.

'They're coming,' a woman shouted. The crowd ran wildly and three people fell under the feet of the crowd.

I can remember nothing of the people running. I was so tired. I fell on the ground near the canal bridge and lay there for some time. And when I sat up, my fear had gone. Had I really run from Martians and escaped death? It didn't seem possible. I began to walk, but my strength had gone and I moved slowly. A train passed and people standing near some houses were chatting. It felt real and familiar and so different from what was happening on Horsell Common.

Sometimes I can have strange feelings, as if I am watching the world and myself from the outside. I felt like this on that night. The countryside was so peaceful compared to the place of death some miles away.

As I was walking home, I met people on the road, a workman carrying a basket and with him there was a little boy. The man wished me goodnight but said nothing about the Martians. I wanted to speak to him but no words came. I walked across a bridge. People were talking at the gate of one of the houses. It felt normal, but behind me there was horror. I stopped when I reached the people. 'What news from the common?' I asked.

'What's it all about?' said the woman.

'Haven't you heard?' I said. 'There are creatures from Mars.'

They laughed when I spoke about the aliens.

'We've heard enough,' said the woman.

I felt angry. 'You'll hear more,' I said and I continued to my home.

My wife was shocked when she saw me. I looked terrible and she made me sit down and gave me a glass of wine.

'There is one good thing,' I said to my wife. 'I don't think the creatures can climb out of the hole.'

My wife's face was deadly white. She believed everything I said. 'They could come here,' she said.

'They can hardly move,' I said. 'Ogilvy told me that Martians can't live on Earth. There is far more gravity here than on Mars and it increases the weight of the Martians' bodies. The Earth's atmosphere contains more oxygen than Mars.'

However I had not considered that these creatures with their mechanical intelligence would find a way to overcome this problem.

The wine and food made me feel strong. 'I think the Martians are afraid because they didn't expect to find living creatures here and they were not expecting intelligent living things. But don't worry,' I said to my wife. 'The army will bomb them.' My dear sweet wife looked at me anxiously.

I didn't know it then, but many strange and terrible days would follow.

Henderson's message about the Martians arrived in London. His editor wrote back asking if the story was true, but because Henderson was dead and no reply arrived at the newspaper offices, the editor decided not to print the story.

Many people in the region had heard of the cylinder, but life continued. People had dinner, men worked in their gardens in the evening, children were put to bed, young people walked hand in hand and students studied. It was as if planet Mars did not exist. At the train stations there were shouts of 'Men from

Mars', but this did not cause any fear. People looking through the train windows saw a strange light dancing and smoke from Horsell Common.

A curious, restless crowd stood watching from a bridge. One or two adventurous people went closer to the Martians, but they never returned. From time to time a light, like the searchlight on a warship, moved across Horsell Common, followed by the heat-ray. Burned bodies lay beneath the stars as the sound of hammering continued. All night the Martians were hammering and working on machines. Greenish-white smoke went into the sky.

It was a Friday night and in the centre of our planet lay a cylinder like a poisoned arrow. [2] In the rest of the world life continued, because they had not heard about the Martian invasion.

Before Stent and Ogilvy were killed, they had sent a message asking the army for help. Soldiers arrived in Woking and took up position around the edge of Horsell Common. Then, a few seconds after midnight, a star fell from the sky into a pine wood. The star was green in colour and looked like summer lightning. It was the second cylinder.

2.　arrow : ◆━━━━━ ▬━

The text and *beyond*

Comprehension check

1 Only one of the sentences is correct. Which one is it? Correct the other sentences.

T F

1 The narrator is not curious about the Martians. ☐☐
2 A Martian is holding a gun on the end of a thin stick. ☐☐
3 The narrator's neighbour thinks these creatures from Mars are beautiful. ☐☐
4 A group of people move towards the Martians with weapons. ☐☐
5 A black shape rises up out of the cylinder and a humming sound begins. ☐☐
6 There are flashes of light, but no one is killed. ☐☐
7 The narrator is afraid of the dawn and the humming sounds. ☐☐
8 The heat-ray kills people slowly. ☐☐
9 No one had escaped the heat-ray. ☐☐
10 The narrator feels strong and moves quickly. ☐☐

2 Complete the sentences with the characters from the box. You can use some character more than once.

> the narrator's wife   Stent   the narrator   the Martians
> Ogilvy   Henderson   a neighbour

1 .... thought the creatures are strange men from Mars.
2 .... was suddenly afraid of the Martians.
3 .... was shocked by the narrator's appearance.
4 .... said the Martians can't live on Earth.
5 .... thought the army will bomb the Martians.
6 .... sent a message about the Martians to London.
7 .... were hammering as they worked on their machines.
8 .... sent a message asking the army for help.
9 .... gave the narrator a glass of wine.
10 .... could hardly move because there is more oxygen than on Mars.

Vocabulary

3 Choose three synonyms from the box for each of the six words. Use your dictionary if necessary.

> tranquil fearless startled restful terror great stunned
> brave extreme interested horror courageous
> nosy panic calm inquisitive strong astonished

1 shocked: ....
2 curious: ....
3 fear: ....
4 intense: ....
5 peaceful: ....
6 adventurous: ....

4 Use the words from exercise 3 to complete the sentences.

> tranquil alarmed fearless curious terror

1 The narrator is afraid of the Martians but he is also ....
2 When the heat-ray kills Ogilvy, Stent and Henderson, the narrator feels real ....
3 The countryside was .... compared to the place of death on Horsell Common.
4 The narrator's wife is .... when she sees her husband.
5 Several .... people approached the Martians but never returned.

5 Match each word (1-5) to its opposite (a-e).

1	☐	calm	**a**	afraid
2	☐	extreme	**b**	agitated
3	☐	fearless	**c**	moderate
4	☐	curious	**d**	hopeful
5	☐	despairing	**e**	indifferent

Grammar

The Past continuous

*Most of the people **were standing** in groups.*

We form the Past continuous with the past form of the verb *be* and the -*ing* form of a verb.

*We **were sitting** in the sunshine.*

We use the Past continuous:

- to talk about an action that was happening at or around a past time:
  *It was evening and people **were staring** at the huge cylinder.*
- to describe a scene in the past:
  *Ogilvy, Stent and Henderson **were moving** towards the cylinder carrying a white flag.*
- for something which happened in the past during another action:
  *When I got home the children **were playing** in the garden.*
- to show that something continued for some time:
  *Everyone **was shouting**.*
- for something that happened again and again:
  *They **were** always **arguing**.*
- with verbs which show change or growth:
  *Her English **was getting** better.*

6 **Write sentences with the following words using the Past continuous.**

1   What / the creatures / do / ?

2   We / watch / the cylinder

3   I / cry / like a child

4   A train passed and people / chat

5   I met people on the road / as I / walk home

6   People / look / through the train windows at the strange light

7   Trees / burn / and branches / fall

8   I felt as if / I look at myself from the outside

9   People / have dinner / and men / sit in their gardens

10   Students / study and young people / walk hand in hand

Bravery proverbs

7 Match the proverbs (1-4) to the correct definition (a-d).

1 ☐ Fortune favours the brave.
2 ☐ Bravery without intelligence is not bravery.
3 ☐ It is easy to be brave from a distance.
4 ☐ Many are brave when the enemy flies.

a You can be brave when you're standing back and watching.
b It's easy to look brave when the enemy is running away.
c Courageous action is often rewarded.
d You have to carry out brave actions in an intelligent way.

Speaking

8 In pairs, discuss the questions.

1 The people who haven't seen the cylinder or the Martians don't believe the story. Why not?
2 Do we only believe in things that we can see for ourselves? Can you give an example?
3 If something fell from the sky and landed near your house, would you look or stay away? Why?
4 Are you brave or are you fearful of unexplained things?

Speaking: Means of transport

T: GRADE 6

9 In H.G. Wells' time most people travelled by train, in carriages, by bicycle and by horse and cart. In pairs, discuss the questions.

1 Do you prefer to travel by plane, boat or train? Why?
2 Would you rather travel by car or by bicycle in your town?
3 Have you ever been on a long distance flight? Where did you go?
4 How do you occupy your time when you are travelling?
5 If you won some money and you could travel anywhere in the world, where would you go?
6 If someone in your family suffered from travel sickness, how would you help them?

Before you read

Vocabulary

1 **Match the words (1-8) to the correct meaning (a-h).**

1	☐	terrified	a	loud sound in the sky when there's a storm
2	☐	to borrow	b	to take something with a promise to return it
3	☐	machine guns	c	to be in an accident
4	☐	war-fever	d	excitement about war
5	☐	thunder	e	very afraid
6	☐	to crash	f	automatic guns
7	☐	to lock	g	to fall down
8	☐	to collapse	h	to close (a door) with a key

2 **Use the words from exercise 1 to complete the sentences.**

1 When a cart .... it falls onto its side.

2 When you ask a friend for a book you .... it.

3 If someone is very scared, we can say they are ....

4 .... often scares animals.

5 Continuous fire comes from ....

6 When people are keen for war to begin they have a kind of ....

7 During war, buildings can ....

8 When you leave your house you .... the door.

Reading pictures

3 **Look at the picture on page 29 and answer the questions.**

1 The narrator is in his garden. Who do you think he is talking to?

2 What can you see in the distance?

3 Do the two people seem anxious?

4 What is the view like from your home? What can you see?

The fighting begins

he next day the weather was hot and I got up early. I stood in my garden looking towards Horsell Common, but I could hear nothing except a bird singing and the sound of a train. My neighbour was in his garden.

'The soldiers will get the Martians today,' he said. 'And we can learn about their planet. We might discover something interesting.' He gave me some strawberries from his garden. 'Cylinder number two landed and the woods are still burning.' My neighbour became sad when we spoke about 'poor Ogilvy'.

After breakfast I decided to walk towards Horsell Common and talk to the soldiers about the Martians. They told me the situation was under control and asked me to describe the creatures.

'Haven't they got necks?' asked one.

I repeated my description of them.

'Like octopus,' he said. 'So we're fighting some kind of fish.'

I was excited by so many army weapons on Horsell Common, but it didn't seem a fair fight. The Martians would be helpless in their hole.

I went home, but while I was having tea with my wife there was a faint explosion. The trees near the local college were on fire and a church collapsed. I realised that our house could be hit by the Martians' heat-ray.

'We can't stay here,' I said to my wife.

My wife was terrified. 'Where can we go?'

'Leatherhead,' I said. 'To my cousin.'

'How can we get there?' she said.

'Wait here.' I ran to the local pub *The Spotted Dog* and paid the owner two pounds to borrow his horse and cart. [1] I promised I'd bring it back by midnight. I drove the horse and cart home and packed a few valuables. My wife, our servant and I set off. In front of us the landscape was sunny, but behind there was thick black smoke and fire. We could hear the machine guns and the crack of rifles. [2]

My wife was silent as we drove to Leatherhead. I could tell she was afraid, but I had felt a strange excitement all day. I can only describe it as war-fever and I wasn't sorry when I returned home that night. I wanted to be there when the army killed the Martians. The night was dark, the sky was blood-red and I saw green fire falling into a field. It was the third falling star.

1.
2. **crack of rifles** : the sound of gunfire.

A storm was coming. Thunder scared my horse and we went down the hill very fast, out of control. And I could see something moving. How could I describe it? It was a huge metal walking machine, taller than many houses. I realised that my horse was moving fast towards a second machine. I had to do something. I tried to stop my horse, but it fell and the cart crashed onto its side. When I stood up, the horse wasn't moving.

The huge metal walking machine moved past me and I had the chance to look at it. It was a machine with tentacles and a section like a head. Its body was made of white metal. It looked like a big fisherman's basket and green smoke came from its legs. I could hear it shouting, 'Aloo, aloo,' to its companion.

For some minutes I lay there in the rain and darkness watching the metal monsters and then I walked towards my house. I pushed through trees and fell. I got up and a little further on, I fell over something soft and realised it was a body. When I looked closer, I recognised the man. It was the owner of *The Spotted Dog*. He was dead.

I hurried to my house and locked the door. I changed my clothes and looked out of the upstairs windows. The whole area near Horsell Common was on fire and smoke hid the Martian shapes. At first I could not see what they were doing and then I saw three big walking machines moving around the sandy hole. Were they intelligent machines or was there a Martian sitting inside each one? The safe world I lived in had become chaos in only a few hours.

I saw a soldier in my garden.

'Do you need somewhere to hide?' I asked him.

'I do.'

'Then come into the house.' The man seemed frightened. He sat at the table, put his head on his arms and cried like a little boy. It was a long time before he could speak.

'There was gunfire on Horsell Common,' he said. 'The Martians were moving towards the second cylinder behind a piece of metal. I was riding my horse and I fell off. When I got up, there was fire all around me and my unit had been completely destroyed by the heat-ray. Two walking machines arrived and killed all the survivors, but I hid under my dead horse until the Martians had gone.'

The man became calmer and I found some food for both of us. Later we went upstairs and looked out of the window. In the distance the Martian's hole seemed bigger and there was green smoke. The fire was almost out, but across the valley were burned houses and trees. All this happened in one night.

It was too dangerous to stay in the house, so the next morning we decided to go to London. The man wanted to return to the Horse Artillery and I wanted to go to Leatherhead and then travel with my wife across to France. However, we knew that between us and Leatherhead was the third cylinder. We took food and drink with us. Outside there was no one. Even the birds seemed silent.

We walked until we met three soldiers on the road.

'What are the Martians like?' asked one.

'They're giants thirty metres high,' my friend replied. 'They have three legs, a metal body and a large head.'

'That isn't possible,' said the soldier.

'You'll see,' said my friend. 'They carry a box that shoots fire and kills.'

'A kind of gun?' asked the soldier.

My friend tried to explain the heat-ray and then we said goodbye and continued on our way. We saw a lot of soldiers preparing arms and canons against the Martians and people running away, but some had underestimated the danger. An old man with a box of flowers didn't understand that he should run before the Martians got there.

'Do you know what's in that forest?' I said pointing at the trees. 'Death. Death is coming.'

When we reached the River Thames, we found an anxious crowd. They wanted to get away, but there weren't enough boats to take everyone. Suddenly we heard guns in the distance and a huge explosion. Four walking machines were moving quickly and coming straight towards us was a fifth walking machine. The crowd stood watching silently.

'Get under water,' I shouted. I ran into the river and saw one walking machine destroy the guns on the other side. When one of the guns hit the walking machine, the crowd cheered, but as the machine fell into the river, the temperature of the water changed. I was standing in hot water and escape was hopeless. People jumped out of the river and the heat-ray killed them as they ran along the riverbank. I couldn't stay there any longer. I climbed out of the river and fell. The Martians could see me and I expected to die. A Martian's foot was near my head, but they were busy taking their damaged[3] friend back to the hole. I don't know how, but I'd escaped. It was a miracle.[4]

---

3. **damaged** : broken.
4. **miracle** : surprising, mysterious event.

The text and *beyond*

Comprehension check

1 **Answer the questions.**

1 What can the narrator hear when he wakes the next morning?

2 Why does the narrator's neighbour become sad?

3 What has landed in the woods?

4 Why is the narrator excited about the soldiers and army weapons on Horsell Common?

5 Why do the narrator and his wife decide to leave?

6 What does the narrator borrow from the owner of *The Spotted Dog*?

7 Where does the narrator leave his wife?

8 What does the narrator see on his way home?

9 What do the metal walking machines look like?

10 The narrator falls over something. What?

2 **Are the sentences true (T) or false (F)?**

	T	F
1 The weather was cold.	☐	☐
2 The narrator talks to his wife in the garden.	☐	☐
3 The narrator's neighbour says that once the soldiers capture the Martians they will learn about Mars.	☐	☐
4 There are lots of army weapons on the Common.	☐	☐

3 Match beginnings of the sentences (1-8) to the endings (a-h).

1 ☐ While I was having tea with my wife
2 ☐ I promised the owner of *The Spotted Dog*
3 ☐ Thunder scared my horse
4 ☐ The walking machine's body
5 ☐ The safe world I lived in
6 ☐ The man became calmer
7 ☐ When we reached the River Thames
8 ☐ I was standing in hot water

a and I found some food for both of us.
b we found an anxious crowd.
c there was a faint explosion.
d and escape was hopeless.
e I'd bring the cart back by midnight.
f had become chaos.
g and we went down the hill very fast.
h was made of white metal.

4 Who did what? Answer the questions.

Who...

1 moved around the sandy hole?
2 was in the narrator's garden?
3 rode his horse and fell off?
4 killed all the survivors?
5 found some food?
6 decided to go to London?
7 wanted to return to the Horse Artillery?
8 asked questions about the Martians?
9 carried a box of flowers?
10 stood watching silently?

Writing

5 PRELIMINARY Read part of an email you received from Carl, your English-speaking friend, and the notes you have made. Write your email to Carl using all the notes. Write your answer in about 100 words.

No, because Mum...

It's my birthday next week too

New message _ ⌞⌝ ✕

From:

To:

It was my best friend's birthday yesterday and we went to a great restaurant.

Do you prefer eating at home or in a restaurant? What's your favourite meal?

Tell me about the best place to eat in your town.

Yes but not vegetarian because...

Village... no restaurants so...

Internet project: science fiction

6 Explore the world of science fiction literature online.

Science fiction tells stories which allow us to question what is possible. Many science fiction books explore how normal characters react when they are facing extraordinary experiences.

Here are some suggestions for books to look for:

- *Brave New World*, by Aldous Huxley
- *The Many Worlds of Albie Bright*, by Christopher Edge
- *Phoenix*, by S.F. Said

Choose one of these books and find out more about it online.

- What is it about?
- When was the book published?
- Where is the book set?
- Can you find out anything about the author?

The Solar System.

The Planet Mars

Welcome to Mars

You'll be interested to know that the weather today has a high of 10 degrees and a low of minus 96. Mars is older and colder than Earth. It's small and rocky and about half the size of Earth. And do you know why it's called the Red Planet? It gets its colour from the rusty [1] iron in the ground.

You'll need a spacesuit with oxygen if you step out of the spaceship, because there isn't much oxygen in the air. The atmosphere is thin. It's mostly carbon dioxide, nitrogen and argon. Mars has a dormant volcano called Olympus Mons, which is the highest mountain on Mars. It's 22 km high. Mars also has a big canyon. Valles Marineris stretches for thousands of miles. And remember… you're not imagining things when you look up in the sky and see two moons. They're called Phobos and Deimos.

---

1.   **rusty** : when something is covered in rust, a red oxide that appears on metal when it has been in water.

Mars and the Victorians

Man has been fascinated by Mars for a long time. Wells' novel *The War of the Worlds* appeared in Victorian Britain, when people wanted stories about Mars. 1877 was an exciting year for research. In August the two planets (Earth and Mars) came close together and astronomers could see Mars quite well. They saw a polar ice cap and some kind of water, which looked like an ocean or a lake. They saw that Mars has weather (dust storms and high-speed winds) seasons and a twenty-four-hour day. Many scientists thought there might be intelligent life on the Red Planet. An American from Boston, Percival Lowell, in 1893 decided to devote his life to astronomy. He built the Lowell Observatory on high ground in Flagstaff, Arizona. From there he could study Mars. He was particularly interested in Giovanni Schiaparelli's ideas. Schiaparelli

was an Italian astronomer who called the Martian seas and continents dark and light areas. He saw channels on Mars and referred to them as *canali*. The mis-translation of this word into English meant that astronomers believed that intelligent life on Mars had engineered large-scale artificial structures or canals. Lowell thought that the Martians who had built them were advanced and very clever.

Percival Lowell.

Other scientists were not so sure. In 1909 scientists studied Mars through a powerful telescope. They thought the channels had been formed naturally by erosion.

NASA and Mars

It wasn't until July 1965 that NASA's Mariner 4 probe took images of Mars. The images showed that the planet is more like the Moon than the Earth. Between 1960 and 1980 Mars was the main objective of the US and Soviet space programmes. In 1971 the Soviet's Mars 3 was the first spacecraft to land a capsule on the planet. In 2001 the US Mars Odyssey orbited it and discovered caves in the volcano. In 2008 the US probe Phoenix landed in the polar region of Mars. It studied the arctic soil and found ice beneath the surface.

NASA's Mission InSight Lander gave the Red Planet its first thorough check-up since it formed 4.5 billion years ago. Scientists were looking at the inner core and how the terrestrial planets formed. InSight had

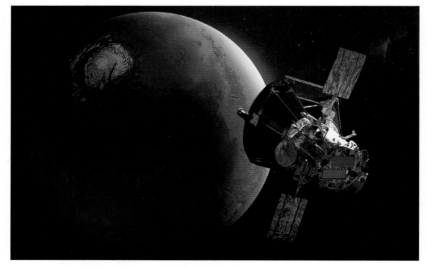

Mission InSight.

a robotic arm, which placed instruments on the surface and then monitored them closely. The instruments drilled [2] into the surface to discover the heat source. Scientists wanted to find out if Mars is made from the same compounds as Earth and the Moon. Another instrument was used which measured the ground for vibrations and 'marsquakes.' The mission hoped to discover why there is life on Earth and if there was once life on Mars.

---

2.   **to drill** : to produce a hole with a machine.

Comprehension check
1 **Answer the questions.**

1   Why is Mars called the Red Planet?
2   Why can't humans live on Mars?
3   What is the atmosphere on Mars made up of?
4   What is the name of the volcano on Mars?
5   What kind of weather does Mars have?
6   Who discovered natural channels in the surface of Mars?
7   Who was Percival Lowell? What did he do for astronomy?
8   What did the Mariner 4 probe discover when it took photos of Mars?
9   What did the InSight Lander mission want to do?

Speaking
2 **In pairs, discuss about space.**

1   Do you believe in aliens? What do you think they could look like?
2   Would you like to go into space? Why? / Why not?
3   Do you think humans will live on another planet one day? Which one?
4   Astronauts say their bodies feel very heavy when they return from space. Why do you think this is?

Before you read

Vocabulary

1 **Match the words (1-8) to the correct meaning (a-h).**

1	☐	pain	**a**	depart on a journey
2	☐	exhausted	**b**	continue on a journey
3	☐	lose your mind	**c**	safe, not hurt
4	☐	keep on	**d**	physical suffering
5	☐	set off	**e**	as fast as possible
6	☐	full speed	**f**	become mad
7	☐	move on	**g**	extremely tired
8	☐	unharmed	**h**	continue doing something

2 **Use the words from exercise 1 to complete the sentences.**

1 It's a twelve-hour journey and we need to .... at 8 am.

2 After a day climbing in the mountains, they were ....

3 Luckily the boy was unharmed after .... to look at something else.

4 A group of people were looking at the painting, but then they .... to look at something else.

5 She went to the doctors because she had a .... in her ear.

6 The train was travelling very fast. It was going ....

7 If you ...., you don't feel mentally strong.

8 .... studying and the exam will be easy.

Reading pictures

3 **Look at the picture on page 47 and answer the questions.**

1 What is the man on the left of the picture doing?

2 What is happening to the two women in the cart?

3 Who is going to help the women?

4 The setting is London. What can you see in the background?

chapter **four**

What happened in London

track 05

he Martians left, carrying their friend and went back to their hole on Horsell Common to await reinforcements.

Every twenty-four hours more cylinders arrived from Mars. By now the army and the navy had realised the power of the invaders. Soldiers positioned their guns all around the cylinder and the hole.

The Martians understood their power and worked hard as they prepared for battle. They moved things from the second and third cylinders to Horsell Common. There was lots of green smoke. The soldiers were also preparing for battle.

I left the fire and smoke and on my way towards London I saw a small boat and climbed in. I followed the river because I knew it was my best chance of escape.

There were no oars, [1] so I used my burned hands to move down the river. I was in pain and tired after my terrible experience. The sun was hot and, when I reached the bridge at Walton, I landed my boat and lay in the long grass, sick and exhausted. When I got up, it was late in the afternoon and I walked for half a mile. I didn't meet anyone and then I fell asleep in the shadow of a tree. When I woke I was so thirsty and there was a man sitting next to me.

'Have you got any water?' I asked him.

'You keep asking for water,' he said.

For a moment we were silent as we stared at each other. I looked strange. I was wearing only trousers and socks and my face and shoulders were black from the smoke.

'What does all this mean?' the man said suddenly. 'I have seen fire and death. Everything has been destroyed, even our church. Why?'

I realised he was a curate. [2] He had escaped from the heat-ray, but now he had lost his mind.

'Are these creatures everywhere?' he asked. 'Have they taken over the earth?'

'I don't know, but there's still hope,' I said.

He stared at me. 'This is the beginning of the end. It's the great and terrible day of the Lord. How can we escape them?'

'Three hours ago one of our guns killed a Martian,' I said.

'But the Martians are servants of God. They have come to destroy the evil [3] on this planet. How can a servant of God be killed?'

---

1. **oar :**

2. **curate :** assistant priest.
3. **evil :** bad.

'I saw it happen,' I said.

The curate looked up at the sky. 'The Martians will soon come this way.'

'Let's follow this path,' I said. 'Northward.'

My younger brother was a medical student working in London. He didn't know about the arrival of the Martians until he opened his newspaper on Saturday. 'Martians had landed near Woking and killed many people', wrote a journalist. But the newspaper said that the Martians wouldn't be able to move because of the gravity of Earth. The cylinder was two miles from my house, so my brother wasn't worried about me.

The general panic over the arrival of the Martians didn't start until Sunday evening. The heading in most newspapers was 'Dreadful catastrophe. Martians. London in Danger.'

Londoners read that these creatures could move faster than people first thought and even the strongest guns could not destroy them. They described the Martians as 'big spider-like machines, a hundred metres high, shooting heat-rays.' And people who were arriving from the destroyed areas described what these terrible Martians were like. My brother could hear the gun shots in the distance, but he went back to his room and fell asleep. The next morning there was a sudden knock at his door. It was the police.

'The Martians are coming!' they said.

It was early on Monday morning and the whole of London was in a panic. My brother took all the money he had in the house and went out into the streets. 'Black smoke. The Martians' rockets send a black and poisonous [4] smoke.' he heard people scream.

---

4. **poisonous** : containing a dangerous substance.

The Martians continued their attack while the curate and I were talking. They moved in a line, speaking to each other in strange sounds. The first soldiers fired and then ran away. The second group of soldiers hit one of the walking machines in the leg, but when two other walking machines came to help, they destroyed the soldiers with their heat-rays. After this the three Martians stood quite still for half an hour until four other Martians arrived and gave each of them a thick black tube.

The curate wanted to run away, but I knew we could not run from a Martian. We hid by the side of the road and when two stopped close to where we were hiding, I watched them.

How much did they know about humans? I asked myself. Did they know that we were good at working together? Did they think they could kill every human?

When the Martians' rockets hit the ground, they released a heavy, black poisonous smoke that killed anyone who breathed it. We watched the fourth cylinder fall from the sky, like a brilliant green meteor, while the Martians were spreading smoke over the countryside towards London. By midnight the trees of Richmond Park were on fire and black smoke covered the Thames.

That was the last day of opposition to the Martians. No army could fight the black smoke. Men died and the black smoke lay above the ground, hiding the dead.

London was in chaos and trains weren't running. My brother stole a bike and reached the edge of London ahead of the crowd of people trying to leave the city. When the bike broke, my brother had to walk and when he heard two women screaming, he ran to help them. Two men were trying to pull them out of their cart. My brother was an expert boxer and he hit one of the men, but when

both men wanted to fight him, he knew he was in trouble. Luckily one of the women had a gun. She fired and the two men ran away. Suddenly my brother was driving the women in a horse and cart to a port. They wanted to get out of England.

There were so many carts on the road and people on foot trying to avoid the wheels. My brother saw a man drop his gold coins. When he tried to pick them up, he fell under the wheels of a cart. There were so many people moving and suffering together.

The Martians kept on destroying railways and killing people with their black smoke. And then news came that a Martian had appeared behind the great clock tower Big Ben and walked down the River Thames. These creatures from Mars now controlled the whole of London.

At last my brother reached the port. He found a boat going to Belgium and bought three tickets. Finally, they felt safe, but as the boat set off a Martian appeared. It was the first Martian my brother had seen. Two others joined the first. And then a warship called *The Thunder Child* went full speed towards the creatures and fired. One of the Martians fell and the warship moved towards the second. This Martian turned the heat-ray on the ship. There was a flash and the Martian fell.

My brother's ship moved on, unharmed, through black smoke and steam. My brother and the women couldn't see anything. It was twilight when the captain cried out and pointed. Something went up into the sky and rained darkness on the land.

The text and *beyond*

Comprehension check

1 Are the sentences true (T) or false (F)? Correct the false ones.

		T	F
1	More cylinders arrived from Mars.	☐	☐
2	Neither the Martians nor the army wanted a battle.	☐	☐
3	The narrator sleeps and when he wakes he's very hungry.	☐	☐
4	He meets a curate who has lost his mind.	☐	☐
5	The curate thinks the Martians are servants of evil.	☐	☐
6	The narrator's brother is a dentist working in London.	☐	☐
7	He read about the Martians in his newspaper.	☐	☐
8	People arrived shouting about the pink poisonous smoke.	☐	☐
9	Inside the walking machines, the Martians kill soldiers with their heat-ray.	☐	☐
10	The fifth cylinder landed.	☐	☐
11	No army could fight the black smoke.	☐	☐
12	London was in chaos but the trains were still running.	☐	☐

2 Match the beginnings of the sentences (1-12) to the endings (a-l).

1	☐ The Martians	**a**	Martian appeared.
2	☐ The curate wanted	**b**	had a gun.
3	☐ The narrator's brother	**c**	he ran to help.
4	☐ When he heard two women screaming	**d**	moved on.
		e	spoke to each other in strange sounds.
5	☐ One of the women	**f**	stole a bike.
6	☐ The Martians now controlled	**g**	Belgium.
7	☐ The narrator's brother caught a boat to	**h**	and a Martian fell.
8	☐ As the boat set off a	**i**	to run away.
9	☐ A warship fired at the Martians	**j**	the whole of London.
10	☐ The narrator's brother's ship		

3 **Who or what do the underlined pronouns refer to?**

1 My brother wasn't worried about <u>me</u>: ....

2 He read that even the strongest guns could not destroy <u>them</u>: ....

3 When he heard two women screaming, he ran to help <u>them</u>: ....

4 Two men wanted to fight <u>him</u>: ....

Grammar

Present perfect

Have they taken over the earth?
We use this tense when we are talking about an action that happened at an undefined time in the past and has results in the present. It is formed from *have / has* and the past participle of the verb. The negative is formed with *haven't / hasn't* (*have not / has not*).
They've been married for ten years.
He hasn't lived in London all his life.

We often use Present perfect with:
- *ever* to talk about experience up to the present and *never* for the negative form:
  Have you ever met Jim?   *No, I've never met Jim.*
- *for* + a period of time
  I have worked here for two years / for six weeks / for a week / for a month / for hours / for two hours.
- *since* + a point in time
  I have worked here since 2019 / since this morning / since last week / since yesterday / since I was a child / since Wednesday / since 2 o'clock.
- *already* (= before now)
  Bill has already done his homework.
- *just* (= a short time before)
  Well, I have just finished it.
- *yet* (= at any time up to now)
  I haven't read that book yet.

4 Write sentences with the following words using the Present perfect.

1 The Martians / just / leave / with their friend
2 Soldiers / already / position / guns / around the cylinder
3 The narrator's brother / just / manage / to catch a boat
4 Since / the cylinder / land / I / see / fire and death
5 The Martian / not destroy / that house / yet
6 Since the Martians arrived / they / take over / Horsell Common and London
7 I / never / see / such evil
8 Have you / ever / witness / an attack like this / ?

Speaking

5 A The narrator's brother had a very difficult journey out of London. What would you do in the following situations? In pairs, discuss the questions.

0 The police tell you to leave your home.
I would leave the house immediately and then I would...
1 You hear people screaming for help.
2 Someone tries to steal your phone.
3 You find a bicycle.
4 You see a creature from space.
5 Someone is chasing you.

B Now write down your answers.

0 If the police told me to leave my home, I would take some money and my phone and leave immediately.
1 If I heard people...

Predicting the story

6 'The Martians are coming'. In pairs, discuss the questions.

1 Will the Martians take over London?
2 After taking control of the UK, where could they go next?

Before you read

Predicting the story

1 **What do you think will happen to the narrator in chapter 5? Choose the most likely event.**

a ☐ He escapes to France. **c** ☐ He hides in a house.
b ☐ He finds his wife. **d** ☐ The Martians capture him.

Vocabulary

2 **Match the words (a-i) to the pictures (1-9).**

a garden shed **d** storeroom **g** beak
b ceiling **e** steam **h** lungs
c smashed glass **f** metal bars **i** seeds

 1 ☐
 2 ☐
 3 ☐
 4 ☐
 5 ☐
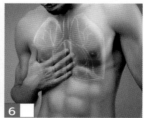 6 ☐
 7 ☐
 8 ☐
 9 ☐

The Earth under the Martians

hile my brother was escaping this country by ship, the curate and I lived in a deserted house to escape the black smoke. We could do nothing but wait for two days. I was worried about my wife and I thought of all the things that could happen to her. She was in Leatherhead and she probably thought I was dead. At least she was with my cousin and not alone, but I did not trust my cousin very much. He was quite slow and didn't always sense danger. My only hope was that the Martians were moving towards London and away from her.

I felt tired and the curate was a very difficult man. He was selfish and afraid, so I didn't want to stay with him. I locked myself in an attic room where I could look out of a window. I saw black smoke drifting past and I saw people in the next house — a face at the window — and I heard sounds of movement. When a Martian passed near us, spraying steam to clear the black smoke, I went downstairs and spoke to the curate.

'We can leave the house,' I said. 'The black smoke has gone.'

'We are safe here,' the curate said. 'Why leave?'

But when I said I was leaving without him, he decided to come with me. We set off at about five o'clock. All along the road to Sunbury were dead bodies, horses and carts covered in black dust. It reminded me of what I had read of the destruction of Pompeii. We walked to the next town. The heat-ray had not hit Twickenham and there was no black smoke. There were people about, but no one could give us any news. We continued on our way, but when we reached Kew, we saw people running and a walking machine appeared. It was close to us and we were in great danger, but it didn't see us. Terrified, we hid in a garden shed until the evening and then we set off again. The Martians were everywhere. We saw one Martian following four or five people, but he didn't kill them. He picked them up one by one and put them in a large metal basket hanging over his shoulder. I realised that the Martians had another purpose for humans.

We ran into a garden and hid behind some trees and at about eleven o'clock we set off again. We passed blackened areas and lots of dead bodies. The curate said he was thirsty and hungry, so we broke into a house to look for something to eat and drink. What luck! There was food in this house. We were sitting in the dark, eating bread and ham when a bright green light filled the kitchen. There was some kind of explosion and I fell unconscious[1]

---

1.   **unconscious** : not being awake.

on the floor. When I woke, the ceiling had come down and there was smashed glass all around us.

'Don't move,' said the curate quietly. 'They are outside.'

We were both quiet. I could hear a metallic sound.

'It's a Martian,' said the curate.

We sat, very still and quiet, until dawn. The house seemed to be covered in a wall of earth and there was a Martian standing guard outside the house. We moved into the storeroom.

'The fifth cylinder has landed here,' I whispered. 'It hit the house last night.'

'God have mercy on us,' said the curate.

Outside I could hear hammering on metal, and then a hissing sound like an engine. We were very hungry and we found some more food. I fell asleep and when I woke, the curate wasn't there. He was in the kitchen, watching the Martians through a hole in the ceiling. Very quietly, I moved towards him. A large piece of the ceiling had come down when the fifth cylinder landed. I could put my head out and see outside. It was lucky we had left the other house we went into when we were looking for food. The fifth cylinder had destroyed that house completely. The cylinder now lay in a very large hole. Earth covered the other houses around us and most of our house, except for the kitchen and storeroom.

Strange creatures were moving slowly over the ground. And I could see something like a metal spider with five legs and tentacles. A Martian controlled its movements, which were complex, fast and perfect. It was using its tentacles to move metal bars and strengthen the walls.

I could see the Martians clearly. They were like nothing on our planet. Their bodies, huge and round, were over a metre in diameter and on the front of each body was a face. The face didn't have a nose, just large dark eyes and a beak. Around the mouth were sixteen tentacles arranged in two groups of eight. These were the hands and at the back of the head was one ear.

When scientists later dissected [2] a Martian, they discovered a simple anatomy. [3] They had large brains, which sent messages to the eyes, ears and tentacles. They had lungs and a heart, but no digestive system [4] because they didn't eat. They took fresh blood from other creatures and injected [5] it into their veins. [6] The Martians had brought two or three creatures with them in each cylinder, as they needed them for food. They had killed them before they reached Earth. I find it interesting that a scientific writer wrote about how the human body could develop in the future. He described a shape and internal structure that was similar to a Martian, long before we knew anything about them. I watched them closely and discovered the Martians were different from humans in three other ways. A Martian never slept because they never felt tired and they were also completely sexless. Young Martians grew like a lily bulb, attached to their parents.

We discovered the third difference between Martians and humans much later. Bacteria, [7] which cause problems on earth, do not exist on Mars. Mars does not have our tumours and cancers and the Martians, when they came here, had no defence against our bacteria.

---

2. **dissected** : cut up to study.
3. **anatomy** : body structure.
4. **digestive system** : the parts of the body that deal with food.
5. **inject** : to use a needle to put medicine into a person's body.
6. **vein** : blood moves through this part of the body.
7. **bacteria** : small organisms that can cause disease.

I watched the Martians working together on complicated tasks. People think they make sounds to each other and communicate by moving their tentacles. But I was certain they exchanged thought through telepathy.[8] The Martians didn't wear any clothes and I realised there were no wheels in any part of the machinery they had brought to Earth, which was unusual. The joints in their machines had sliding parts.

Later I discovered that the vegetable kingdom on Mars isn't green, but a vivid blood-red. In fact the Martians brought seeds with them — a plant with red leaves — which grew very quickly.

I was fascinated by these strange creatures and I watched the Martians for a long time. When the curate asked to have a look, we changed places. Later, when it was my turn to watch, I saw a machine at work. I realised there was no one telling it what to do.

---

8.   **telepathy** : to communicate with someone with your mind.

The text and *beyond*

Comprehension check

1 **Put the events in the correct order of time (1-8).**

a ☐ They watch the Martians through a hole in the ceiling.

b ☐ They see Martians collecting men in a basket.

c ☐ They understand that the fifth cylinder landed on part of the house.

d ☐ When the Martians clear the black smoke, it's safe for the two men to leave.

e ☐ A machine is making metal bars.

f ☐ 1 ☐ The narrator and the curate live in a deserted house.

g ☐ They hide in a garden shed.

h ☐ They go into another house and find food, but suddenly there's an explosion.

2 **Answer the questions.**

1 Why is the narrator worried about his wife?

2 The curate is not an easy person to live with. Why?

3 What do they see along the road to Sunbury?

4 What happens to the narrator when there's an explosion?

5 Which rooms are not covered by earth?

6 What did scientists later discover about the anatomy of the Martians?

7 What did scientists later discover about how the Martians ate?

8 Why have the Martians brought creatures with them?

9 How are Martians different from humans?

10 How do young Martians grow?

3 In chapter 5 there is a description of the Martians. What do they look like? Use the words in the box to complete the sentences.

> beak   ear   face   round   hands   dark   mouth   nose

1 Their bodies are huge and ....
2 On the front of their bodies is a ....
3 They don't have a ....
4 Their eyes are large and ....
5 They have a ....
6 Each Martian has sixteen tentacles around its ....
7 The tentacles are their ....
8 At the back of their head is an ....

4 PRELIMINARY Read the text in each box. What does it say? For each question, choose the correct answer (a, b or c).

1
Busy Bee Services
Is your house dusty?
And in need of attention?
Call the Busy Bees

1 This advert is for
a ☐ local honey.
b ☐ dust sheets.
c ☐ a cleaning company.

2
Wall-e from Mars
makes re-usable paper
from waste

2 Wall-e is a robot which
a ☐ recycles.
b ☐ makes chocolate.
c ☐ creates sculptures.

3
The Fifth Cylinder Has Landed
Now showing in all cinemas
Rated PG 13
Some scenes are not suitable
for children under 13

3
a ☐ No scenes will upset children.
b ☐ Adults only.
c ☐ Parents must be cautious with children under 13.

4

> All new arrivals
> must report
> to Cylinder 1

4 The Martian's notice is giving

a ☐ some advice.

b ☐ an instruction.

c ☐ a warning.

5

> *Dear Curate,*
>
> *I'm rationing the food. We haven't got very much left. Can you eat what's on your plate tomorrow and no more?*
>
> *Thanks*

5 The narrator leaves a message for the curate.

a ☐ The curate can have more food.

b ☐ The curate must only eat what the narrator gives him.

c ☐ The curate must eat less food.

Vocabulary

5 Match the descriptions (1-5) to the materials (a-e).

1 ☐ very small dry particles	a	steam
2 ☐ vapour and gases	b	metal
3 ☐ a white vaporous mist	c	dust
4 ☐ a hard substance like iron or steel	d	glass
5 ☐ windows are made of this	e	smoke

6 Use the words from exercise 5 to complete the sentences about the story.

1 We lived in a deserted house to escape the black ....

2 A Martian came near the house spraying ....

3 Along the road were dead bodies, horses and carts, covered in black ....

4 He picked the humans up and put them in a .... basket.

5 When I woke the ceiling had come down and there was smashed .... all around us.

7 Read the paragraph about invasion literature at the end of the 19th century. Choose the correct words.

In the 19th century British people (**1**) *afraid / feared* invasion (**2**) *to / by* Germans, from political extremists and even from aliens. From the 1870s (**3**) *until / through* the beginning of the First World War many people were afraid that (**4**) *the / a* British army wasn't very strong and (**5**) *these / this* island could be invaded by France or Germany. Many authors wrote (**6**) *about / of* this. William Le Queux's book *The Invasion of 1910* told the story of Germany taking over London. Wells developed the invasion novel with his Martians who were technologically superior (**7**) *from / to* anyone on Earth. Wells (**8**) *told / said* that he wanted people to realise the danger of big guns and poisonous gas. After the First World War and the terrible battles of Ypres and the Somme, Wells said, 'the world knows better now.' In his book *The World Set Free* (1914), he said there (**9**) *should / could* be worse horrors when scientists understand how to (**10**) *do / make* atomic bombs.

Speaking: rules and regulations

T: GRADE 6

8 The narrator can't understand the Martians and he doesn't know if they have any rules and regulations. In pairs, discuss the questions.

1 What rules and regulations are there at school and at home?
2 If rules are necessary for society, what rules will you insist that we keep?
3 Do you think there are too many rules in your country?
4 Have you ever broken a rule? What happened?
5 If it's up to you to make rules in the future, which rules will you make?

Speaking

9 The author compares the scene along the road to Sunbury to Pompeii after the destruction in 79 AD. In pairs, discuss the questions.

1 What do you know about Pompeii? How was it destroyed? Who lived to tell the story?
2 How can we compare the black smoke and the heat-ray to the destruction of Pompeii? Why is it different?

Before you read

Vocabulary

1 **Match the words (1-12) to the correct meaning (a-l).**

1	☐ bold	**a**	to say that something is wrong
2	☐ to ration	**b**	to speak softly
3	☐ survival	**c**	to become smaller in size
4	☐ horrified	**d**	not fearful
5	☐ to contract	**e**	an underground room
6	☐ coal	**f**	to disagree violently
7	☐ a cellar	**g**	very shocked
8	☐ an animal's trunk	**h**	to allow small amounts of food
9	☐ disciplined	**i**	controlling the way you live and work
10	☐ to complain	**j**	black rock which burns in a fireplace
11	☐ to argue	**k**	an animal's long nose
12	☐ to whisper	**l**	the state of continuing to live or exist

2 **Use the words from exercise 1 to complete the sentences.**

1 The narrator has to .... the food.
2 The curate is hungry and they .... about food.
3 The curate is .... when the Martians bring the first men.
4 Their only chance of .... is to stay in the house until the Martians have gone.
5 When a Martian comes inside the house, the narrator hides in the ....
6 He can see the Martian's tentacles moving like an elephant's ....

Reading pictures

3 **Look at the picture on page 64 and answer the questions.**

1 Where are the narrator and the curate?
2 What is the narrator doing?
3 Who do you think is outside?
4 Does the curate look anxious? How can you tell?

What we saw from the ruined house

track 07

hen a second walking machine arrived, we were frightened, so we moved from the kitchen into the storeroom. We were afraid that this Martian, standing in a different position, might see us. However, as time passed we became bolder. It was dangerous, but the curate and I wanted to watch the Martians through the hole in the ceiling. We were companions, but the curate and I were very different in character. I told the curate we had to ration the food so we had enough for the days ahead, but he didn't listen. He cried for hours and ate more than I did. Our only chance of survival was to stay in the house until the Martians had left. The curate didn't listen to me and his carelessness put us both in danger. I am ashamed to say that I became very angry with the curate and hit him.

I continued to watch the Martians. There were three new walking machines and they had brought another machine, which dug the ground with its two hands and made metal bars from the earth on the ground. Between the time when the sun set and the stars appeared in the sky, this machine made more than a hundred white metal bars.

The curate was watching the Martians through the hole in the ceiling when the walking machines brought the first men in their baskets. I saw the curate move suddenly backwards. He was horrified and couldn't watch, but my curiosity gave me courage. I looked through the hole in the ceiling. There weren't many stars, but there was a green fire in the Martian's hole. The metal walking machine contracted its legs and I heard human voices. I could see a Martian in the head of the walking machine, the oil of his skin, his bright eyes. Suddenly a long tentacle reached into the basket on his back. There was a scream. A man, who was middle-aged and well-dressed, was lifted out of the basket. His arms and legs moved as he tried to get away. His eyes were staring. He disappeared into the hole and there was silence. Then came a scream and the Martians laughed.

I put my hands over my ears and ran into the storeroom. That night I tried to think of an escape plan, but I couldn't discuss anything with the curate. We were in a difficult situation, but there was always hope. There was no reason for absolute despair. I considered digging my way out, but I knew the curate wouldn't help me. I hoped and prayed that the Martians would leave that place and move on to another town.

We stayed there for several days. I tried digging a tunnel, but when the earth collapsed, it made a loud noise and I was too afraid to continue. I lay on the floor for a long time. One night I heard the sound of heavy guns — six, then another six — and that was all. I didn't think the soldiers could kill the Martians.

On the sixth day of our imprisonment I heard the curate eating and drinking in the storeroom. I told him we had to be disciplined or there would be nothing to eat. I divided the food into rations to last for ten days. I would not let him eat anymore that day. All night he complained he was hungry and for the next few days we argued and fought. He was losing his mind, and also my own mind was strange in those days. I had terrible dreams whenever I slept.

On the eighth day, the curate began talking aloud and not whispering. I could not make him be quiet. He believed God had sent the Martians to punish humanity for its sins and for all the evil on Earth.

'I'm hungry. I want food,' he said to me. 'I'll shout and bring the Martians here.'

That scared me. He slept a little, but when he woke he started speaking loudly again.

'Please be quiet,' I said.

'I must speak the word of the Lord.' The curate ran towards the kitchen. 'I'm going. I know what I must do.'

I saw a large heavy meat knife hanging on the wall. I took it and ran after him. I hit him on the head, but only with the handle of the knife. The curate fell on the ground. He was dead.

Suddenly I heard a noise. I saw the machine that made metal bars moving slowly across the hole in the ceiling. Then I saw the large dark eyes of a Martian looking down and a long metallic tentacle came through the hole in the ceiling. I turned and stood

behind the door watching the tentacle twisting and turning. Then I went quietly into the storeroom and opened the door of the coal cellar. I stood in the darkness. Had the Martian seen me? What was it doing?

Something was moving. I could hear someone pulling a body across the kitchen floor towards the opening. I went quietly towards the door and looked into the kitchen. I saw a Martian examining the curate's head. It knew that someone else had hit the curate. I went back into the coal cellar, shut the door and covered myself in coal and bits of wood. Soon I heard a soft metallic sound and something moved into the storeroom. I hoped that the Martian's tentacles could not reach me, but a tentacle moved across the cellar door and opened it. In the darkness I could see the tentacle like an elephant's trunk moving towards me. It examined the walls, the coal, the wood and the ceiling. It touched my boot and I wanted to scream, but I bit my hand. I heard a click. The tentacle had taken something — a piece of coal — to examine.

When I thought it had gone, I moved under the coal. Then I heard the Martian coming back, moving towards me. It touched the walls and the furniture. Then it closed the cellar door. I heard it go into a food cupboard. I could hear it opening the biscuit tins and then a bottle smashed. There was a long silence. Had it gone? All day I hid amongst the coal. Only on the eleventh day was I brave enough to come out.

The text and *beyond*

Comprehension check

1 **PRELIMINARY** **For each question choose the correct answer (a, b, c or d).**

1   The narrator rationed
    a ☐ sweets.
    b ☐ time.
    c ☐ food.
    d ☐ wine.

2   The curate was careless and the narrator
    a ☐ didn't listen to him.
    b ☐ ignored him.
    c ☐ played a game with him.
    d ☐ became angry and hit him.

3   A long tentacle
    a ☐ extinguished the green fire.
    b ☐ took a man from a basket.
    c ☐ sprayed black smoke.
    d ☐ picked up a metal bar.

4   On the eighth day the curate
    a ☐ stopped eating.
    b ☐ ate all the food.
    c ☐ began talking loudly and not whispering.
    d ☐ fell asleep.

5   The narrator picked up a heavy meat knife and
    a ☐ hit the curate on the head.
    b ☐ threw it.
    c ☐ attacked a Martian.
    d ☐ stabbed the curate.

2 Put the events (a-h) in the correct order of time (1-8) to make a summary of the second part of chapter 6.

a ☐ A tentacle touched my boot.

b ☐ The Martian examined the curate's head.

c ☐ On the eleventh day I came out.

d ☐1☐ I saw a Martian's dark eyes looking down.

e ☐ The Martian took all the food in the cupboard.

f ☐ I could hear someone pulling a body across the floor.

g ☐ I covered myself in coal.

h ☐ I went into the storeroom.

Vocabulary

3 A Complete the table.

Verb	Noun	Adjective
survive		surviving
think		thoughtful
	complaint	complaining
cry	cry	
divide	division	
scare		scary
act		acting

B Complete the sentences with words from the table.

1 When someone reflects about things they are ....

2 Their only chance of .... was to stay in the house.

3 The curate found the Martians ....

4 The curate was always .... he was hungry.

Speaking

4 We all have fears. In pairs speak about what you are afraid of.

1 Were you afraid of anything when you were a child?

2 Is there anything that scares you now?

3 Have you ever overcome a fear? How did you do it?

Grammar

Past simple vs. Past perfect

*Our only chance of survival **was** to stay in the house until the Martians **had left.***

- We use the **Past simple** to talk about something that started and finished at a definite time in the past. We often use it with dates and times and words like *yesterday*, *last* and *ago*.

- We use the **Past perfect** to refer to a time before another past time. By using the Past perfect we make the order of events clearer.

  *Pete no longer owned a bike, he **had sold** it.*
  *I recognised the town, I **had been** there before.*

  *We arrived at 8 pm, but they **hadn't eaten** dinner.*

- We often use the Past simple with *when*, *before*, *after*, *by the time* and the Past perfect in the main sentence.

  ***When** I arrived at school they had already started the test.*
  ***By the time** I reached the station, I had missed the train.*

5 Complete the sentences with the Past simple and Past perfect forms of the verbs in brackets.

1 When the firemen .... (*arrive*), the fire .... (*go*) out.

2 Ella .... (*buy*) a birthday cake, but her mum .... (*already get*) one.

3 Before they .... (*visit*) Thailand, they .... (*never see*) such beautiful beaches.

4 Charles .... (*already study*) Italian, before he .... (*move*) to Rome.

5 When I .... (*start*) my job, I .... (*be*) married for three months.

6 By the time she .... (*reach*) the age of forty, she .... (*became*) a millionaire.

Culture Spot

Wells and the British Empire

The War of the Worlds shows Wells' concerns about the British Empire. The Martians' colonisation of southeast England is a parallel to how the British used their technological superiority to rule other countries. The British Empire was the largest, richest and most powerful Empire in world history. Over three centuries Britain brought lands from every continent under its rule. In 1497 England established a settlement in North America through the voyage of Giovanni Caboto. He wanted to find a trade route to Asia, but landed in New-found-land and claimed it for England. In 1600 Elizabeth I granted a charter to the East India Company and they began establishing trading posts in India. The first permanent English settlement on the continent was in Jamestown, Virginia, in 1607 and the first in Africa was in 1661 at James Island. It was a key post in the slave trade. The explorations of Captain Cook (1768, 1772 and 1776) meant that Britain had settlements in Australia and New Zealand. Nine tenths of this first British Empire was in America, but after a bitter war, America won its independence in 1783. Twenty-five years after the loss of the American colonies, a second and more extensive British Empire began to grow. Britain controlled Canada, Australia, New Zealand, South Africa, much of Malaya and Sierra Leone. In about 1875 a period called the New Imperialism began. Benjamin Disraeli, Queen Victoria's Prime Minister, bought shares in the Suez Canal to make sure there was trade access to India and East Asia. However the Empire began to unravel. The self-governing Dominion of Canada was formed in 1867, Australia in 1901, New Zealand in 1907 and South Africa in 1910. India did not have a new constitution until 1935.

Read the paragraph and answer the questions.

1   Where did Giovanni Caboto establish a settlement?
2   What did he want to find?
3   What did the East India Company do?
4   In which trade was James Island a key post?
5   When did America win its independence?
6   Why did Disraeli buy shares in the Suez Canal?
7   When did India have a new constitution?

Before you read

Predicting the story

1 **In pairs, discuss the questions.**

1 Do you think the Martians have gone? Why?
2 There is no food in the house. How can the narrator survive?
3 What do you think will happen next?

Vocabulary

2 **Match the words (a-f) to the pictures (1-6).**

a weed   c a pile of earth   e a roofless house
b blinds   d shady tree   f ruins

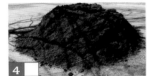  

3 **Match the words (1-4) to the correct meaning (a-d).**

1	deaf	a unable to think clearly
2	confused	b strange
3	dry	c needing water
4	weird	d unable to hear anything

4 **Use the words from exercise 3 to complete the sentences.**

1 When the ground is hard and dusty it is ....
2 The atmosphere on the moon is different to earth and quite ....
3 When someone has just woken up they can seem ....
4 If someone can't hear anything they could be ....

73

chapter **seven**

The stillness

here was no food in the house. The Martians had taken everything and for two days I had nothing to eat or drink and I began to despair. At first my mouth and throat were dry, I had no energy and felt very tired. My mind didn't work very well. I thought I was deaf because I couldn't hear any sounds of movement coming from the hole where the cylinder had landed. I wanted to crawl quietly to the hole in the ceiling, to see what the Martians were doing, but I was afraid and I didn't feel strong enough.

On the twelfth day I was so thirsty that I took some rainwater from the pump [1] next to the sink. The colour of the liquid was black, but I drank two glasses of water. It made me feel much

---

1. **pump :**

better. The pump made quite a lot of noise, but while I was in the kitchen I didn't see any tentacles. The Martians hadn't heard me. On the thirteenth day I drank some more water, but when I slept I had horrible dreams filled with ghosts and tables covered in food. I thought about the curate and how he had died, but most of all I wanted water, more water. And the light that came into the storeroom was not grey, but red. And to my strange, confused mind it was the colour of blood.

On the fourteenth day, when I went into the kitchen, red Martian weed had grown across the hole in the ceiling and on the fifteenth day I could hear the sounds of a dog scratching. I could see the dog's nose through the red weed. My first thought was that I could kill the dog and eat it.

'Good dog,' I said softly. But the dog disappeared. I was so hungry I could eat anything.

Then I had a second thought. I had heard the dog, so I couldn't be deaf. And there were no sounds coming from the Martians. I lay for a long while listening. I heard the dog moving about and birds singing in the trees. Finally, I put my head through the hole in the ceiling and looked out. Crows were fighting over dead bodies, but the Martians were gone. I looked all around me. The machinery had gone and all that remained was blue powder, metal bars and skeletons. I climbed out through the red weed and looked about. There were no Martians anywhere. I began to tremble. I could escape. I waited for some time, but I needed to see further. So I climbed to the top of the pile of earth that had buried the house when the fifth cylinder landed. I looked all around, but there were no Martians anywhere.

When I had last seen this area, before the Martians arrived, the street had been full of comfortable red and white houses and

shady trees. The Martians had destroyed these red and white houses, but not completely. They hadn't burned the trees and houses with their heat-ray. The walls of the houses still stood, but the doors and windows had been smashed and red weed grew in their roofless rooms.

The day was bright and the sky was bright blue. A breeze blew the red weed and the air smelled sweet. I had spent fifteen days in a dark and ruined house and now I was looking at a weird landscape, a place in ruins. It was like looking at another planet. Everything had changed and I was no longer master of my own planet, but an animal amongst other animals, controlled by the Martians. My life had changed. Like a wild creature I watched and ran and hid. Man and his empire was over.

My most urgent concern was hunger. I saw vegetables growing on the other side of a red-covered wall. I climbed the wall and pulled up onions and carrots. A little further on I found mushrooms growing and I ate them. Then I went on my way through trees covered in red weed towards the district of Kew. I was surprised in this hot dry summer to find water, but then I realised that the tropical red weed grew quickly when it found water. It grew thickly in the River Wey and the River Thames and when I reached Putney the bridge was covered in red weed.

I have to add a note at this point in the story about the red weed. It was not able to live long on our planet. There are bacteria on planet Earth that killed the red weed quite quickly. It was ironical that the water, that had helped it to grow so rapidly, carried the dead weed out to sea.

The first thing I did when I found water was to drink. I drank a lot and then I tried to eat some of the red weed, but it had a

horrible metallic taste. I continued walking and at last came to Putney Common. In some parts, the houses were undisturbed. They had their blinds down and their doors closed and I imagined the owners were out for the day or asleep. Here there was less red weed. I hunted for food in some of the houses, but found nothing. Other people had come into these homes and had taken all the food.

I was tired and hungry and I lay near a tree for the rest of the day. I had travelled quite a distance, but I had met no humans, just a couple of hungry dogs. When it became dark I walked along the road to Putney, where the Martians had used the heat-ray. In a garden near Putney I found some potatoes and ate them. In the evening light, the place looked so different. I could see black trees, black ruins and the river red with weed. The worst thing of all was the silence.

Change had come so quickly. It was terrifying. Maybe the Martians had killed everyone. Maybe there weren't any humans left on Earth and I was the last man alive. At the top of Putney Hill, I found a skeleton. Its arms were not with the rest of the body. I was certain that all humans had been killed in this part of the country. Maybe the Martians had moved on somewhere else in search of food. They could be destroying Berlin or Paris or moving northwards.

The text and *beyond*

Comprehension check

1 **Match the beginnings of the sentences (1-10) to the endings (a-j).**

1 ☐ I couldn't hear any sounds,

2 ☐ I got some rainwater

3 ☐ The light that came into the storeroom

4 ☐ Red weed had grown

5 ☐ I could hear the sounds of a dog

6 ☐ Crows were fighting

7 ☐ The Martians' hole

8 ☐ I was hungry and

9 ☐ I met no one, just

10 ☐ I was certain that all

a I found some vegetables growing.

b scratching.

c some hungry dogs.

d across the hole.

e humans had been killed.

f was empty.

g so I thought I was deaf.

h from the pump.

i over dead bodies.

j was the colour of blood.

2 Answer the questions.

1 What does the narrator need more than anything else?
2 What does he think when he sees the dog?
3 What can he see when he looks outside?
4 What was the street like before the Martians came?
5 What does the area look like now?
6 What food does the narrator find?
7 What will happen to the red weed?
8 Where does he think the Martians have gone?

Speaking

3 In pairs, discuss the questions.

1 The narrator's mind isn't working very well. Why do you think this is?
2 What does the narrator dream about? Have you ever had a dream like this? Describe it.

Grammar

Adverbs of manner

'Good dog,' I said **softly**.

We usually make an adverb of manner by adding -ly to the adjective form.

For adjectives of more than one syllable ending in -y, change the y to i:

happy — happ**ily**

Some adverbs of manner are irregular:

good — **well**

fast — **fast**

hard — **hard**

4 Write the adverbs for the adjectives.

1 anxious: ....

2 beautiful: ....

3 gentle: ....

4 good: ....

5 immediate: ....

6 lucky: ....

7 loud: ....

8 quick: ....

9 quiet: ....

10 sad: ....

11 sweet: ....

12 violent: ....

5 Use the adverbs from exercise 4 to complete the sentences.

1 I wanted to crawl q.................... to the hole to see if the Martians were there.

2 The pump made a lot of noise. The water came out l.................... .

3 I heard birds singing s.................... in the trees.

4 I looked a.................... through the hole.

5 The Martians had gone so I i.................... set off.

6 L.................... I found some vegetables to eat.

7 Change had come so q.................... .

8 The Martians could be destroying Paris v.................... .

Speaking: health and fitness

T: GRADE 6

6 The narrator is eating raw vegetables to survive. In pairs, discuss the questions. Before you start, make a list of the words you might need.

1 What do you need to eat to have a healthy diet?

2 Is your diet good? What do you usually eat?

3 It's healthy to eat five portions of fruit and vegetables each day. Do you have your 'five a day?' What must this include?

4 How much water do you drink every day?

5 Why is physical exercise important?

6 What can you do if you want to keep fit?

7 Do you do some exercise everyday? What?

8 What could you do to improve your health and fitness?

Orson Welles' radio dramatisation of The War of the Worlds

It was 8 pm on 30th October 1938, the night before Halloween. Orson Welles, a young theatre star who went on to become a famous film director, was about to lead ten actors and an orchestra in a radio programme called *Mercury Theatre on the Air*. Before the era of TV, people sat in front of their radios and listened to music, news and radio drama. Millions of Americans usually tuned in to this drama programme, but unfortunately not many of them were listening at the start of the programme when the announcer said this was an original dramatisation of the 1898 H.G. Wells science-fiction novel

The War of the Worlds. Using the format of a simulated news broadcast narrated by Welles, the programme started with some music, before an announcer interrupted with urgent news: 'Ladies and gentlemen, we interrupt our programme to bring you a special news report from the Intercontinental Radio News. At twenty to eight, there were reports of several gas explosions on planet Mars. We know that this gas is hydrogen and something is moving towards the Earth at great speed.'

The radio announcer was on the roof of the Broadcasting Building in New York city and continued: 'Can you hear the bells? They are telling people to leave the city because the Martians are coming. There's so much traffic on the road. Don't go near any bridges. They are all blocked. The air force, army and their guns have all been destroyed. Everything... gone. This is the last broadcast you will receive, but I'll stay here to the end...'

The announcer said that a Martian spacecraft had crashed into a farm in New Jersey. Martian cylinders were falling all over the United States. The first walking-machine reached land and stood looking over the city of New York. He waited for the other walking-machines, which stood like sky-scrapers. They lifted their metal hands and sprayed black smoke over the city. People saw the smoke and ran towards the Hudson River. Thousands jumped into the river like rats. The smoke reached Times Square and even though people tried to run away, the smoke got them and they fell.

For the next hour, actors played the parts of army officials and astronomers. One actor sounded like the president of the United States, which made it seem even more real.

At the end of the radio drama, Orson Welles spoke on air. He told listeners that the drama had been the radio station's way of dressing-up in a white sheet for Halloween.

But in the 1930s, after the Great Depression, people were used to feeling afraid and anxious. They were used to news reports interrupting radio programmes. There had been the Hindenburg disaster a year earlier, when a German passenger airship caught fire during landing and was destroyed. There had also been a hurricane in New England a few weeks before Orson Welles' radio play. People were worried about the threat[1] of war in Europe.

The next morning after the radio broadcast, newspapers said there had been panic because of the fake reports.

'Radio Listeners in Panic, Taking War Drama as Fact', was the headline in the *New York Times*.

'US Terrorised by Radio's Men From Mars', wrote the *San Francisco Chronicle*.

'Fake Radio Scares Nation', wrote the *Chicago Herald*.

Newspapers reported that thousands of terrified New Yorkers had left their homes. There was a rumour[2] that several people had been

---

1.   **threat** : a great danger.
2.   **rumour** : gossip that may or may not be true.

treated for shock in a hospital in New Jersey. The Washington Post newspaper said that a man died of a heart attack because of the programme. No one knows if this story was true. Police records show there was an increase in calls, two thousand in less than two hours, on the evening of 30th October. Some people wanted to find out where they could give blood. Some wanted the electricity company to cut off the power to their city to keep it safe from Martian invaders. We know now that the reports were exaggerated. [3]

The newspaper industry was not happy about the success of radio. Radio was a new media and because of its popularity newspapers now felt it was a threat. The newspapers could see this as an opportunity to criticise the radio.

'Radio is new, but it has adult responsibilities,' wrote the *New York Times*. Newspapers talked to many different people and created a story of mass hysteria. [4] They published [5] the photo of a woman who had broken

---

3. **to exaggerate**: to say that something is worse or more important than it really is.
4. **mass hysteria**: a group of people are very anxious or very excited.
5. **to publish**: to print in a newspaper or book.

her arm. They said she was scared when she heard about the black smoke in Times Square, so she ran out of her apartment and fell.

At a press conference in November 1938, Orson Welles said how shocked he was at the public reaction. He said he was sorry.

Soon after this Welles directed the film *Citizen Kane*, the story of Charles Foster Kane (played by Welles) who wants to control people in the same way as he controls his media empire. The radio play might have influenced Welles. The American Film Institute named it as the greatest film of all time.

Comprehension check

1 **Answer the questions.**

    1 What did people do before the era of TV?

    2 What was happening in the radio programme when the announcer interrupted?

    3 What did the special report from Intercontinental Radio News tell people?

    4 Why were American people afraid and anxious in the 1930s?

    5 How did some people react to the radio drama?

    6 Why did the newspapers exaggerate the reports?

    7 Was the radio play a disaster for Orson Welles and his career?

    8 What is interesting about Charles Foster Kane's job?

2 **Discussion. In pairs, look at the statements and discuss the questions. Report back to the class with your ideas.**

    • We live in a time of fake news. What is fake news?

    • Where can we read it?

Before you read

Vocabulary

1 **Match the words (a–f) to the pictures (1–6).**

a	cricket	**c**	mud	**e**	bus shelter
b	sword	**d**	dawn	**f**	cage

 1 ☐

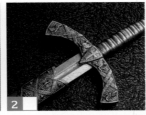 2 ☐

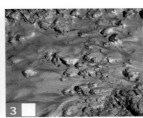 3 ☐

 4 ☐

 5 ☐

 6 ☐

2 **Use the words from exercise 1 to complete the sentences.**

1 In summer we play .... on the village green.

2 When it's raining I can wait for the bus in the ....

3 My hamster lives in a ....

4 I love getting up early to watch the ....

5 Children love playing in puddles and walking in ....

Reading pictures

3 **Look at the picture on page 93 and answer the questions.**

1 What is the setting?

2 What can you see at the top of the hill?

3 What do you think has happened?

ᗡead London

I spent the night in a pub at the top of Putney Hill and slept in a bed for the first time in weeks. Before I went to bed I searched for food and found two tins of pineapple, some biscuits and old sandwiches. I was afraid a Martian might find me so I didn't light any lamps and I didn't sleep very well. My brain felt stronger because of the food and three things occupied my mind: what had happened to the curate, where the Martians could be and what had happened to my wife.

I didn't feel responsible for the death of the curate. He wanted to tell the Martians we were hiding there, so I had to hit him. But I couldn't stop thinking about him. I went back in my mind over our conversations, over everything that had happened. I have been honest and I have written my whole story including the curate's death. The reader can judge if I was right or wrong.

I thought about the Martians. I thought about my wife. Was she dead? How had the Martians killed her? I imagined a hundred different scenarios. I sat up in bed staring at the dark. I prayed that the heat-ray had been quick and she had felt no pain. I hadn't prayed in all these weeks, but now I did. I had become an animal and when dawn came I went out of the house, like a rat leaving its hiding place. I understand how animals feel now and I hope this experience makes us kinder towards poor creatures that we dominate.

That morning the sky was bright. I saw carts abandoned on the road and destruction all around. I still wanted to get to Leatherhead and find my wife, but I knew that she and my cousin were either dead or had run away. I felt so lonely.

I walked to Wimbledon Common and I was surprised there was no red weed there. I stopped to watch some little frogs and suddenly realised there was a man with a sword near some bushes. I approached him slowly and he looked at me silently. The man's clothes were dirty. He was covered in green slime and dried mud and at first I didn't recognise him.

'Stop,' he shouted when I was close. 'Where do you come from?'

'From Mortlake,' I said. 'I hid in part of a house. When a cylinder landed it hit the house and buried it in earth.'

'There is no food here,' he said. 'This is my area and there's only food for one. Which way are you going?'

'I'm going to Leatherhead, to find my wife.'

'Oh, it's you,' the man said.

I recognised him at the same moment. 'You are the soldier who came into my garden!' We shook hands. 'Have you seen the Martians?'

'They have built a flying machine and green stars keep arriving,' he said. 'I think humanity is finished. The Martians have beaten us and we're just ants now.'

I sat staring.

'Soon the Martians will begin catching men. They'll choose the best and put them in cages,' said the man.

'I'm not sure I want to live anymore?' I said.

The soldier looked at me. 'I want to live and I've got a plan. So many people don't have any spirit or any dreams and they are the ones who are perfect for the Martians' breeding[1] programmes. Those people will be happy to live in a cage. They will become the Martians' pets. The Martians will train them to hunt other humans.'

'That's impossible,' I said. 'We should do something. What plans do you have?'

'I want to live underground. The London drains[2] are big and there are cellars and railway tunnels. I need clear-thinking people with me, no one who is weak or silly. Those kind of people should die. We will live underground in London and when the Martians are away we will be able to come out of our tunnels and play cricket. And we must find all the books we can and keep them underground. Some of us can become spies and watch the Martians, but it is important that the Martians think that we are kind and no threat to them.'

For a while I believed in his ideas for the future. He took me to the house on Putney Hill, where he was living. He showed me the tunnel he was digging, but it was very small. I helped him dig, but he seemed lazy and soon wanted us to stop. We

---

1. **breed** : when animals produce babies.
2. **drains** : area below the ground for rain water.

had dinner and the soldier opened a bottle of champagne. We played cards and then I went onto the roof to see the green lights and the fires near Kensington. I could see a strange purple light. What was it? I was sure it was caused by the red weed. I stayed on the roof for a long time thinking about the soldier. He was a dreamer with big plans, but he was too lazy. I would go to London without him.

In London the streets were silent and there was black dust and bodies everywhere. I first heard the sound of the Martians at South Kensington, just two notes like a cry, 'Ulla, ulla.' The voice became stronger and stronger. It seemed to come from Regent's Park. I was tired, hungry and thirsty as I walked in this city of the dead. I found some food and drink in a pub and I slept on a sofa. That terrible cry was still in my ears when I woke. 'Ulla, ulla.' I had taken biscuits and cheese with me and when I reached Baker Street I saw a Martian in his walking machine above the trees. I watched him for some time, but he didn't move. Why was he standing and shouting?

Further on I found the machine that could make metal bars in the middle of the road. It had been smashed. And near Primrose Hill I saw a second Martian in his walking machine standing quite still. Then the sound of 'Ulla, ulla,' stopped suddenly. I was terrified and I hid in a bus shelter, but when dawn came my courage returned and I went back to Primrose Hill. There was a third Martian at the top of the hill and he wasn't moving. I walked towards him and as I got closer I saw black birds flying around his head. Suddenly I wasn't afraid. I ran up the hill towards the silent Martian, wild and happy.

The Martians were dead, killed by bacteria. They died like

the red weed because there's no bacteria on Mars. It was when these invaders drank and fed on Earth that our bacteria began its work.

Nearly fifty Martians were dead. I stared at the great walking machines, so powerful and complex. I looked from the top of Primrose Hill over London and thought of all the people who had built this great city. The invasion was over. All the people who had run away would return. I put my hands up to the sky and thanked God.

The text and *beyond*

Comprehension check

1 Are these sentences true (T) or false (F)?

		T	F
1	After three weeks the narrator sleeps in a bed.	☐	☐
2	He eats some food but his mind still feels weak.	☐	☐
3	He regrets hitting the curate.	☐	☐
4	He hopes the heat-ray killed his wife quickly.	☐	☐
5	The narrator feels like a hunted, wild animal.	☐	☐
6	Near some bushes, he meets a man with a gun.	☐	☐
7	They recognise each other.	☐	☐
8	The soldier doesn't have a plan.	☐	☐
9	The soldier has been working very hard on a tunnel.	☐	☐
10	The narrator takes the soldier with him to London.	☐	☐

Vocabulary

2 Read the paragraph about the soldier's ideas for the future and complete it with the words from the box.

> cricket   humans   cellars   cages   spy   afraid   tunnels   pets

Once the Martians are in complete control, they will be able to manipulate some of the humans they capture. They will be the people without any spirit or dreams. They will be the people who are too **(1)** .... to fight back. They will allow the Martians to keep them in **(2)** .... and they will become the Martians' **(3)** .... The Martians will teach these weak people how to find other **(4)** .... and hunt them down.

The soldier wants to live underground in **(5)** .... and in London railway **(6)** ...., where there is a lot of space. He will become a **(7)** .... and watch the Martians and when they are not in London, he and the other people in his group will play **(8)** .... in the open air.

3 PRELIMINARY **Read the text and decide which answer (a, b, c or d) best fits each gap.**

We all experience fear sometimes. There are times when we're afraid and we need to find some courage. It's important how we deal with fear. Courageous people believe in (1) .... They know they have strong values and are confident (2) .... the challenges in life. Courageous people are passionate and they have (3) .... mental and moral (4) .... They can remain strong in a situation where there is danger or difficulty. Physical courage is bravery (5) .... the face of physical pain. Everyone should start each day with a (6) .... courage.

1	**a** himself	**b** herself	**c** ourselves	**d** themselves
2	**a** about	**b** in	**c** by	**d** through
3	**a** big	**b** large	**c** great	**d** small
4	**a** strong	**b** big	**c** powerful	**d** strength
5	**a** to	**b** in	**c** of	**d** with
6	**a** small	**b** little	**c** tiny	**d** big

4 **The narrator speaks about places in London. Find out about these places online. Then match each place (1-6) to the correct definition (a-f).**

1 ☐ The Thames

2 ☐ Regent's Park

3 ☐ Baker Street

4 ☐ Primrose Hill

5 ☐ The Tube

6 ☐ Big Ben

a at its top is one of the six protected viewpoints in London

b the big clock in Westminster

c underground trains

d one of the royal parks

e where fictional detective Sherlock Holmes lived

f the river that flows through London

Speaking: learning a foreign language

T: GRADE 6

5 The Martians speak a strange language. They cry 'Ulla, ulla.' In pairs, discuss the questions.

1 Why do people learn foreign languages?

2 Which is the most difficult language to learn? Why?

3 What do you find most difficult about learning English?

4 What could you do in order to improve your vocabulary?

5 Does learning English help you to understand films and your favourite songs?

6 Are you learning English in order to use it in a job in the future?

7 Do you think it's ever possible to speak English like your mother tongue language?

8 Can you learn more English inside or outside the classroom?

9 If you travel to an English speaking country, will you practice your spoken English as much as you can? How?

10 So as not to offend people of different cultures, what kind of things do you need to do?

Writing

6 Choose one of the characters in the story and write 100 words about him or them. You can use some of the words below.

Narrator: brave, caring, broken, curious, intelligent, clear-thinking

The soldier: a dreamer, lazy, idealistic

Martians: aggressive, merciless, technologically advanced, conquerors, cruel, clever

The curate: cowardly, weak-willed, greedy, selfish

Describe what you think the character looks like.

Before you read

Vocabulary

1 **Match each stretch of water (1-3) to its geographical position (a-c).**

1 ☐ The Irish Sea
2 ☐ The Atlantic
3 ☐ The Channel

a separates Southern England from Northern France.
b is on the west side of Great Britain.
c separates North and South America from Europe and Africa.

2 **Match the words (1-3) to the correct meaning (a-c).**

1 ☐ devastation
2 ☐ terrestrial species
3 ☐ argon

a animals that live on land
b a gas
c chaos

3 **Use the words from exercise 2 to complete the sentences.**

1 When there is a war, houses, land and countryside are destroyed and when the war ends there is ....

2 Acquatic species live mostly in water, but .... live mostly on land.

3 The black smoke in this story has a type of gas in it called ....

Predicting the story

4 **In pairs, discuss the questions.**

1 What has killed the Martians?
2 Do you think more Martians will arrive?
3 What do you think the narrator will do now?
4 Do you think his wife is alive?

Devastation and joy

track 10

he Martian invasion was over. People heard this news all over the world because a man went to St Martin's-le-Grand and sent a message to Paris. People in a thousand cities, who were afraid the Martians would invade their towns and homes, were delighted at the news.

In Great Britain people cried with joy and church bells rang all over the country. Food arrived for us from across the Channel, from across the Irish Sea and from across the Atlantic. Countries sent us corn and bread and meat.

But I became very unwell and I can't remember the next three days. I walked the streets, crying, and a kind family took me into their home. When they found me, they said I was singing, 'I'm the last man alive. Hurrah!'

When I seemed a little better they told me that the Martians had destroyed Leatherhead and the people living there were all dead. I felt sad and lonely.

I stayed four days with them and they were kind to me, but I had to go home. I promised I would visit them again and when I left I had tears in my eyes. It was strange to see shops open and so many people in the streets. Their faces were full of energy, but they still wore their dirty clothes.

I bought a newspaper. The first one to publish news was *The Daily Mail*. They were not able to print much, but one thing interested me. Scientists had examined the Martian machines and said that those creatures from Mars had discovered the 'secret of flying'.

I walked to Waterloo station and caught a train. I sat alone in a compartment and watched the devastation through the window. The buildings in London were black from the black smoke, and hundreds of people were working on the railway line. I saw the sixth cylinder with a pile of earth against it. People stood all around it and a Union Jack flag flew above the cylinder.

I got off the train at Byfleet and had to walk from there. I passed the broken cart that crashed in the storm. I walked through the pine wood where red weed grew neck-high. I passed the place where the owner of *The Spotted Dog* had fallen. I was glad his body had been buried.

When I arrived at my house I looked at it with hope, but then any hope disappeared. The front door was broken, the study window was open and inside the house felt empty. I went into my study. On my desk was the paper I had written when the first cylinder fell. My sentence ended with my vision for the future: 'In about two hundred years we may expect...' It was almost a month ago.

I remember that day very clearly. I had stopped writing and met the newspaper boy at the gate. I listened to his tale about 'Men from Mars.' It seemed an unbelievable story.

I walked from the study to the dining room. There was meat and bread on the table, from the supper I had had with the soldier when I found him in my garden. Everything was as I had left it. And then a strange thing happened. I heard a voice.

'It's useless,' said the voice. 'There's no one in the house.'

I turned. The patio windows were open and I went into the garden. There was my cousin and my wife. She gave a soft cry. She looked pale and faint. 'I knew you would be here.' She fell and I caught her in my arms.

This is the end of my story and I'm sorry that I cannot give the reader better answers. There are so many questions about the Martians and we don't know how to answer them all. After the war, doctors examined the Martians' bodies and found only the bacteria of terrestrial species. No one knows how the Martians made the heat-ray or the black smoke. Scientists found an unknown element in the black smoke. The Martians mixed it with argon to make a deadly compound which attacked blood.

People can see a specimen of a Martian at the Natural History Museum in London and look at drawings. But the question everyone continues to ask is, 'Will the Martians attack again?' I think they might. We need to discover the exact position of the gun that fires the cylinders from Mars, so that we can tell when a future attack could happen. Next time we need to destroy the cylinder before it becomes cool and the Martians appear. Maybe I am wrong about another invasion of Earth. Maybe the Martians have turned their attention to other planets.

chapter nine

Before the Martians arrived, Man thought he was the only life form in the universe. Maybe we have learned something from this Martian invasion. Our planet is no longer safe. We know that good or evil could arrive at any moment from space. But it's also possible that the Martians on Mars will not return. It may be safer for them to invade Venus. It's also possible that Man could land on Venus, when the sun cools and Earth becomes too cold for us to live on.

Sometimes, when I'm writing in my study, I have visions of the Martian invasion and see fire in the valley. I go out in the street and look at the children going to school, at a workman on a bicycle and it seems unreal. Sometimes at night I see the black smoke in the dark silent streets and bodies lying on the ground. I wake up cold and afraid in the darkness of the night. I go to London and see crowds of people. They seem like ghosts of the past in a dead city.

The day before writing this last chapter I stood on Primrose Hill and looked at the houses in the distance and at people walking by. I watched visitors standing around the Martian machine that is still there. And I remembered when I was last there on that great final day.

I have learned so much from the Martian invasion, but what is most important to me is to hold my wife's hand. She thought I was dead and I thought she was. After all that has happened we have each other.

The text and *beyond*

Comprehension check

1 **Answer the questions.**

1 How did the world learn that the Martian invasion was over?
2 How did people in Great Britain show their happiness?
3 What happened to the narrator at the beginning of chapter 9?
4 What did the narrator find out in *The Daily Mail* newspaper?
5 What did the narrator's house look and feel like when he returned?
6 What did he find in the dining room?
7 Who did he find in the garden?
8 What element did scientists find in the black smoke when they analysed it? What does this element do to the human body?
9 Where can people see a specimen of a Martian?
10 What does the narrator think the government should do next time the Martians arrive?

Internet project: climate change

2 **Use the internet to find information about climate change and what we can all do to help. Use the following questions to help your research. Write a report and tell the class about your findings and ideas.**

1 Scientists predict that ice caps will melt. What effect could this have on life on earth?
2 Could climate change destroy life on Earth?
3 What's a carbon footprint? How can we reduce it?
4 Find examples of how we can 'go green'.
5 Should we all drive 'eco cars'? Find examples of these cars.
6 Make a list of energy sources and their effect on nature. What energy sources should we use?
7 Have you changed your lifestyle to save the planet? What have you done?
8 Wells predicted climate change in 1898 with this story. He suggested that Earth could become too cold. We're experiencing global warming. What can we do to make a difference?

Identifying emotions

3 **Why do the characters behave the way they do in the story? Match the beginnings of the sentences (1-6) to the endings (a-f).**

1 ☐ The narrator is sensible because   **a** he's hungry.

2 ☐ The curate behaves strangely   **b** kill a man and then laugh.

3 ☐ The curate is horrified because the Martians   **c** he rations the food.

4 ☐ The curate is careless because   **d** a Martian is looking for him.

5 ☐ The narrator is terrified because   **e** because he is losing his mind.

Speaking

4 **In pairs, discuss the questions.**

1 Do you think there are other forms of life in space?

2 Could visitors from space land on Earth?

3 What lessons can we learn from this fictional story?

4 If aliens landed on Earth, would you be brave like the narrator or anxious like the curate? How would you behave?

5 **You are visiting another planet. In pairs, discuss the questions.**

1 What does it feel like as you step onto this planet?

2 Concentrate on the senses. What can you see?

3 Can you hear anything? What?

4 Can you smell anything? Are the smells cleaner and fresher than planet Earth?

5 Does the air taste of anything?

Writing

6 **Send your family a postcard from a planet you have landed on.**

- Tell them what you are doing.
- Tell them what you have seen.
- Describe a new kind of animal that you've seen.
- Describe the colours on the planet.

War of the Worlds

Before you read

1 *Look at the pictures and answer the questions.*

1. Who do you think the people are in picture A? What do you think they are looking at?

2. Do they seem happy or anxious? How can you tell?

3. Can you describe the room in picture B? Whose bedroom do you think it is?

4. Looking at Pictures A and B, how do you think the film is different from the book?

When people asked the film director Steven Spielberg why he had wanted to adapt H.G. Wells story for the big screen, he said he thought it would be fun to make 'a really scary film with really scary aliens.' The film is based on the book by H.G. Wells, but it is no longer set in Victorian England. Spielberg sets it in the period following the 9/11 terrorist attacks in the US. The film also marks this terrible time in history and how the US reacted to it. In the film there's an aeroplane that crashes and a board with names and photos of missing friends and family. American audiences in 2005 found the movie frightening. H.G. Wells' tripod walking machines were fiction, but the terrifying and shocking terrorist attacks in 2001 had been real. *The War of the Worlds* is about humanity's deepest fear: the threat of annihilation. [1]

Spielberg changed parts of the story to create the film. The protagonist is played by Tom Cruise, who takes the part of the narrator in the book. In the film he has a name, Ray, and he is a divorced father, who is trying to protect his two children (the actors Justin Chatwin and Dakota Fanning) from a violent alien invasion. Like the book, the main character is not interested in fighting aliens. All he wants is to survive each day and to keep his children safe.

Steven Spielberg is a master when it comes to action and special effects. He is brilliant at creating tension and understands the audience's desire to see what's happening on the other side of a locked door. Spielberg likes to shock by showing the audience houses that have been destroyed and the land covered in red weed.

But Spielberg also struggled to come up with a decent ending as he believes Wells did too. The walking machines collapse without warning and a dying Martian's hand appears. Ray and his family are reunited.

---

1.   **annihilation:** the destruction of something.

Comprehension check

1 Answer the questions.

1   When and where is the film *War of the Worlds* set?
2   Why did American audiences find the movie frightening in 2005?
3   According to the text, what is humanity's greatest fear?
4   How is the protagonist in the film different from the protagonist in the book? How is he similar?
5   Why is Spielberg considered a brilliant director?

Picture summary

1 Look at the pictures from the story and put them in the correct order of time.

A ☐

B ☐

C ☐

D ☐

E ☐

F ☐

G ☐

H ☐

I ☐

Comprehension check

2 Put the events (a-j) in the correct order of time (1-10).

a ☐ The Martians are dead, killed by bacteria.

b ☐ The narrator drives his wife to his cousin's and meets a soldier.

c ☐ They watch the Martians feeding on the blood of men.

d [1] Lights in the sky look like a meteor, but it's a cylinder and it lands on Earth.

e ☐ The Martians leave and the narrator escapes. He meets the soldier again.

f ☐ Oily, grey creatures climb out of the cylinder and kill people with their heat-ray.

g ☐ When the narrator arrives home, his wife is there.

h ☐ On his way to London, the narrator meets a curate.

i ☐ A family takes the narrator in.

j ☐ A cylinder destroys part of the house they're hiding in.

3 Who said this? Match each sentence to a character. You can use some character more than once.

curate   narrator   soldier   narrator's wife
Ogilvy   a neighbour

1 There are men inside who need to get out: ....

2 What ugly creatures. What strange men from Mars: ....

3 The soldiers will get the Martians today: ....

4 Where can we go? How can we get there?: ....

5 I hid under my dead horse: ....

6 Do you know what's in that forest?: ....

7 Everything has been destroyed, even our church. Why?: ....

8 I'm hungry. I want food: ....

9 Some of us can become spies and watch the Martians: ....

10 I knew you would be here: ....

4 **Match the words (1-6) to the phrases that refer to the story (a-f).**

1	☐ genre	**a**	the narrator
2	☐ setting	**b**	the Martians
3	☐ climax	**c**	19th-century England
4	☐ protagonist	**d**	first-person
5	☐ antagonist	**e**	when the Martians conquer London
6	☐ type of narration	**f**	science fiction

Listening

🔊 track 11

5 **You will hear 12 statements about the story repeated twice. Complete the statements with the missing words.**

1 Earth is .... than Mars and anyone living on Mars is more ....

2 The Martians looked at the possibility of living on Earth because the .... was too .... on Mars.

3 One night a cylinder .... on Earth.

4 A creature appeared with tentacles like grey ....

5 I saw a group of .... lifting their flag of .... The Martians killed them with their heat-ray.

6 The Martians couldn't move on Earth because oxygen increased the weight of their ....

7 The Martians .... huge metal walking machines with a section like a ....

8 The curate believed the Martians had .... to destroy all the .... on the planet.

9 The Martians had rockets that released black poisonous .... , when they hit the ground.

10 The two men hid in a house and .... the Martians through a .... in the ceiling.

11 The curate wanted to .... and bring the Martians into the house, but the narrator .... him.

12 Just like the red weed, the Martians were killed .... bacteria on Earth.

Writing

6 Look at the clues and complete the crossword.

```
            1           2    3
            D      5    D    T
        4 [W][ ][ ][R][ ]  [ ] [ ]
            [ ]     [ ]   [ ] [ ]
        6 [A][ ][ ][ ][ ][ ][ ][ ][ ]
     7      [ ]     [ ]        [ ]
   8 [H][ ][ ][ ]   [ ]    9   [ ]
     [ ]    [ ]     [ ]        [ ]
     [ ]    [ ]  10 [ ]    12  [ ]
     [ ]    [ ] 11 [C][ ][ ][S][ ]
  13 [C][ ][ ][ ][ ][ ][ ][ ]  14 [B][ ][ ][ ]
            [ ]             [ ]
                           [ ]
```

1 destruction

2 sunrise

3 shake because you are frightened

4 strange

5 to limit food

6 someone who studies the stars

7 to make a sound like a snake

8 noun from *hot*

9 very big

10 a horse pulls this

11 we keep animals in these

12 when a fire burns it produces flames and...

13 the Martians fall to earth in this

14 a weapon that explodes

7 Do you agree with some opinions about the story? Why / Why not?

1 The narrator didn't need to visit Horsell Common when the Martians landed.

2 No one expected gas warfare.

3 Most aliens probably look like humans.

4 The army was well-prepared for a sudden invasion.

5 The soldier had thought of a good plan.

6 The Martians will probably return one day.

7 The Martians are a political symbol for revolution.

8 People are compared to rats, showing that the human race isn't well developed.

9 The red weed is a physical metaphor for all the blood spilled during war.

10 The destruction of London is compared to the destruction of Pompeii in ancient times.

8 PRELIMINARY Your English teacher has asked you to write a story. Your story must begin with this sentence.

When I woke up this morning, there was a spaceship in my garden. I went outside and...

Write your story in about 100 words.

Speaking: true values

9 The narrator says he has learned so much from the Martian invasion, but what is most important is to hold his wife's hand. In pairs, discuss the questions.

- What do you appreciate about your everyday life?
- Do you feel connected to your community and surroundings? How?
- Do you feel valued? Give some examples.
- Do you have a feeling of control and freedom over your life?
- Many people believe that mindfulness or meditation can help people feel more content and enjoy each day. They think it can help your general well-being and mental health. What helps you?

This reader uses the expansive reading approach: where reading is not only the enjoyment of the story and the discovery of a new language, but an opportunity to make cultural connections.

The new language introduced in this step of our **Reading & Training** series is listed below and language from lower steps is included too. For a complete list for all six steps, see The Black Cat Graded Readers Handbook at *blackcat-cideb.com*.

Step THREE B1.2

Verb tenses

Present Perfect Simple: unfinished past with *for* or *since* (duration form)
Past Perfect Simple: narrative

Verb forms and patterns

Regular verbs and all irregular verbs in current English
Causative: *have / get* + object + past participle
Reported questions and orders with *ask* and *tell*

Modal verbs

Would: hypothesis
Would rather: preference
Should (present and future reference): moral obligation

Ought to (present and future reference): moral obligation
Used to: past habits and states

Types of clause

2nd Conditional: *if* + past, *would(n't)*
Zero, 1st and 2nd conditionals with *unless*
Non-defining relative clauses with *who* and *where*
Clauses of result: *so; so ... that; such ... that*
Clauses of concession: *although, though*

Other

Comparison: *(not) as / so ... as; (not) ... enough to; too ... to*